The Obsessive Personality

The
Obsessive Personality

ORIGINS,
DYNAMICS
AND
THERAPY

Revised Edition

Leon Salzman, M.D.

Professor of Clinical Psychiatry
Georgetown University School of Medicine

JASON ARONSON, INC.
NEW YORK

*To my wife and children, and to
my patients over the past 25 years.*

SECOND EDITION, *December 1973*
Second Printing, March 1975

Preface

The obsessive-compulsive personality structure is the most prevalent characterological
type, and the extremes of this personality organization constitute
by far the bulk of the psychiatrists' patients. Yet, not all obsessive
personalities are functioning inadequately nor are all compulsive
individuals so maladjusted as to require psychiatric therapy.

Because Freud used the hysterical personality structure as the
paradigm for his theoretical conceptions of psychic functioning,
many psychiatrists and behavioral scientists have tended to assume
that the hysteric was more prevalent and that the qualities attributed to the hysterical defense were characteristic of neurotic
disorders. There is little doubt that even a superficial perusal of
the obsessive style described in this book will find an immediate
identification in every reader. This implies not that we are all obsessives but that the *defense* is universal and ubiquitous and in some
measure participates in all human functioning.

The obsessional defense is an attempt (albeit an illusory one) to deal with man's essential powerlessness and helplessness in both his control over his own physical being and over the physical world around him. In the latter case, he has only limited and minimal influence, and even in the former, his control can be exerted only over his voluntary musculature. When the obsessional defense is successful it achieves some illusion of security and strength in an uncertain and unpredictable life.

The value of the obsessive-compulsive defense for the maintenance of adequate functioning in man has been stressed by all behavioral scientists. Man's physical deficiencies and mental limitations leave him susceptible to profound uncertainties about his future—with inevitable feelings of helplessness and insecurity. Not only does he have limited control over the forces of nature (despite the scientific advances in the last century) but he is also incapable of controlling his own intellectual and emotional responses. He is often at the mercy of the "out-of-awareness" ideas and impulses that propel him into action. The existential problems that face him constantly and the knowledge of his limited span of existence and the certainty of his own death are things about which he can do very little—except to construct illusions.

In the face of these realistic and inevitable problems confronting all mankind, many people have the additional burden of increased insecurities and uncertainties caused by early experiences or traumatic events that accidentally occurred in their lives. The uncertainties of childhood, produced by inconsistent and sometimes malevolent familial situations, can only compound the widespread insecurity caused by financial crises or economic or political disasters. Such difficulties complicate man's inevitable human frailties and frustrate his attempt to control his existence.

In the face of these universal and contradictory demands, the obsessive-compulsive techniques by fantasy or realistic manipulation of oneself and the outside world maintains an illusion of having greater control over one's life than is actually so, thereby decreasing the feeling of ultimate impotence, an existential fact that plagues man.

Occasionally, these defensive techniques become so pervasive and the need for guarantees and certainty so extreme, that productive living can be seriously interfered with. We may then be dealing with an obsessional neurosis or the breakdown of the obsessional defenses producing depression or schizophrenia.

The bizarreness and striking nature of such extreme states have been described through the ages, but none have done so as masterfully as Freud. In his early descriptions of this disorder* he said, "Obsessional neurosis is shown in the patient's being preoccupied with thoughts in which he is in fact not interested, in his being aware of impulses in himself which appear very strange to him and in his being led to actions the performance of which gives him no enjoyment, but which it is quite impossible for him to omit. The thoughts (obsessions) may be senseless in themselves, or merely a matter of indifference to the subject; often they are completely silly, and invariably they are the starting-point of a strenuous mental activity, which exhausts the patient and to which he only surrenders himself most unwillingly. He is obliged against his will to brood and speculate as though it were a question of his own important vital problems. The impulses which the patient is aware of in himself may also make a childish and senseless impression; but as a rule they have a content of the most frightful kind, tempting him for instance, to commit serious crimes, so that he not merely disavows them as alien to himself, but flies from them in horror and protects himself from carrying them out by prohibitions, renunciations and restrictions upon his freedom. At the same time, these impulses never—literally never—force their way through to performance; the outcome lies always in victory for the flight and the precautions. What the patient actually carries out—his so called obsessional actions—are very harmless and certainly trivial things, for the most part repetitions or ceremonial elaborations of the activities of ordinary life. But these necessary activities (such as washing, dressing, or going for a walk) become extremely tedious and almost insoluble tasks. In

* Sigmund Freud, "Standard Edition of the Complete Psychological Works," vol. XVI, p. 257.

different forms and cases of obsessional neurosis the pathological ideas, impulses and actions are not combined in equal proportions; it is the rule, rather, that one or another of these factors dominates the picture and gives its name to the illness, but the common element in all these forms is sufficiently unmistakable."

To paraphrase Freud's comments, certainly this is a crazy illness. Freud goes on to say, "The most extravagant psychiatric imagination would not, I think, have succeeded in constructing anything like it; and if it were not observed every day one would never bring oneself to believe in it. However, the therapist should not suppose that he will help the patient in the least by calling on him to take a new line or to cease to occupy himself with such foolish thoughts and to do something sensible instead of persisting in playing childish pranks. He would like to do so himself—he is completely clear 'mentally' and shares the professional's opinion of his obsessional symptoms; he even advances such assessments spontaneously. But he cannot help himself. What is carried into action in an obsessional neurosis is sustained by a kind of energy about which we probably know nothing compared with our understanding of normal mental life. There is only one thing the patient can do: he can make displacements and exchanges, he can replace one foolish idea by another somewhat milder one, he can proceed from one precaution or prohibition to another, and instead of one ceremonial he can perform another. He can displace the obsession, but he cannot remove it. An ability to displace any symptom into something far removed from its original conformation is a main characteristic of the illness."

In addition to the polarities and extremes of feelings and behavior, doubt enters the intellectual life and—little by little—it begins to gnaw even at what is usually felt to be certain. This ends up in an ever-increasing degree of indecision, loss of energy, and restriction of freedom. The obsessional neurotic is often extraordinary self-willed and, as a rule, he has intellectual gifts above the average. He has usually reached a high level of ethical development and exhibits over-conscientiousness and is more than ordinarily "correct" in his behavior.

This is a most accurate picture and I will enlarge upon these characteristics and integrate them into the main activity of the obsessional (throughout the book the term *obsessional*, for reasons of convenience, will be used to mean obsessive-compulsive) which is to gain control and mastery over himself and avoid the recognition of his fallibility and weakness. The obsessional technique, through its elaborate devices of avoiding commitments and decisions, never exposes one to the realization of the possibilities of failure and thus avoids the awareness of imperfection, fallibility, and humanity. The attempt at omniscience and omnipotence, coupled with an elaborate verbal set of defenses, gives one the illusion of having superhuman powers to guarantee one's future. If the verbal magic fails, then the ritual—with its possibilities of overcoming the human limitations—attempts to achieve such guarantees. Finally, if all else fails, the individual can by developing phobias absolutely avoid any encounter with situations or objects which endanger his sense of control.

The ritual which characterizes the compulsive syndrome is dramatic in its absurdity and tenacity in spite of every wish and desire to abstain from its performance. However elaborate it might be, it is essentially a technique of control similar to the rituals in all religious systems, where the fulfillment of the ritual is designed to influence or control some higher being to perform tasks in our behalf which are beyond our own capacity to accomplish.

When it serves to enhance and support one's security, the obsessive mechanism can play a significantly productive role in one's living. The issue is one of the degree to which the illusory mechanisms and perfectionist patterns cloud the reality to the extent that they obstruct the individual in his efforts to perform the necessary tasks for adequate living. If one comes to believe and accept his superhuman fantasy and overlooks his human limitations, he may end up denying all reality and becoming psychotic.

On the other hand, as I will expand in the succeeding chapters, everyone utilizes such defensive techniques—some more and some less. The term "obsessed" is used so casually in daily conversations that it has lost the intensity of its meaning in a psychiatric sense. In common parlance it is used to denote any sustained, devoted, and intense interest in any matter. While the dictionary defines obsession as an "abnormal preoccupation with an idea or feeling," it does not clarify at what point preoccupation is abnormal. Devotion to an idea or cause, with persistent efforts to actualize it, does not automatically make it abnormal or an obsession. Doubting and being unable to commit oneself does not necessarily indicate obsessive living. Being scrupulously clean or passionately orderly with perfectionistic desires does not imply an obsessional concern with order. Yet, such manifestations *might* indicate neurosis. As the expression "to be obsessed" has taken on a pejorative meaning and implies some mental disorder, its use can both discourage and disparage some sincere and creative efforts. We must, therefore, be clear about the healthy and the pathological elements of dedication—as well as the limits of preoccupation before such characteristics interfere with productive living. To do a masterful job in any area, from carpentry to astronomy, requires a dedication that insists on the highest performance. This involves scholarship as well as total participation in the doing, and may demand the totality of an individual's time and effort. This is not obsessional behavior and may be entirely contrary to it. It may be a freely selected activity to which one commits one's skills and interests. This is in direct contrast to the obsessional preoccupation in which one is "imprisoned," unable to shift and change, and fearful lest any involvement or commitment leave one vulnerable and endangered. It is interest by default, even though at times it may be strong enough to result in many useful products. It is the negative of the creative process.

Yet, in the spectrum that ranges from the effective use of obsessional techniques to the extreme states of neurosis lies the area for psychiatric understanding that would be applicable to all areas of human knowledge. The therapy of the extreme states constitutes the bulk of this book, since clinical issues and case material are widely used to demonstrate my point of view. Psychoanalytic therapy which developed out of Freud's study of the hysterical personality was applied to this defensive structure with mixed and indecisive results even after prolonged therapy. It is my contention that by taking a fresh look at the symptomatology of this fascinating and pervasive human condition we can apply new techniques and therapeutic interventions that have been amassed since Freud originally described his therapeutic approach, and thereby increase our chances of success while drastically reducing the time needed for this accomplishment.

The dilemma is this: How can we utilize a patient's interest and determination to rid himself of distressing symptoms when his efforts to do so invariably take on the compulsive characteristics that have made him ill in the first place? Likewise, how can the therapist in his dedication to resolve his patient's dilemma avoid being trapped in his own compulsive tendencies? In addition, the requirements of the therapeutic process to be open, free, spontaneous, and willing to experience new insights is anathema to the obsessional. His illness is a concerted effort to do the opposite. How can we change an individual's behavior when his goal is to make his present behavior anxiety-free rather than to abandon the patterns that inevitably produce anxiety? These and many other therapeutic issues are discussed at length since, despite all the obstacles, only psychotherapy has the possibility of altering these symptoms.

In recent years, it has been possible to understand the effectiveness of some philosophical approaches like Zen, or a Japanese form of psychotherapy called Morita Therapy, in their emphasis on "achieving by not forcing oneself to do." It is in essence the only way to abandon compulsive behavior, since to instruct, encourage, or assist a compulsive individual to change his behavior by admonition that it is in his interest to do so, will only exaggerate the problem. Zen and Morita advocate a "non-doing," or letting it happen.

The success of behavioral therapy in relieving some of the symptoms and the more consistent benefits of paradoxical intention in these disorders attest to the value of a realistic approach to behavioral modification by a slow but regular process of dealing with specifics rather than global attitudes. Paradoxical intention by encouraging a patient to expand or embellish his disturbed behavior is saying in effect we don't want you to change but actually to get worse. In doing so we have taken some of the compulsive needs to change away from the patient, allowing change to come on its own. It is from such approaches rather than from the highly intellectualized compulsive therapeutic approaches, that success in dealing with these disorders may come.

In proposing some newer conceptions about the obsessive-compulsive defensive techniques, I do not intend to replace other formulations. Nor am I saying that it is the only view of this mechanism that is fruitful and correct. Rather it has been extremely useful to me in highlighting many questions which heretofore were either clouded in mystery or inadequately comprehended by other formulations.

Perhaps my presentation can serve to stimulate therapists and patients alike to a more spontaneous curiosity, which is the prime essential in the treatment of the obsessional states.

Contents

PART   I

characteristics
of the obsessive
personality

CHAPTER 1

Theories
of Obsessive
Behavior

C urrent conceptions of the etiology and therapy of mental disorders are of surprisingly
recent origin. Each year brings forth a vast collection of books,
articles, and research reports which cast doubt on older theories
and suggest alternative explanations to the hitherto cherished
formulations. This is a healthy process, because we have not yet
arrived at final statements about most mental disorders.

HISTORICAL PERSPECTIVES

Until Sigmund Freud began his investigations of hysteria
and other neurotic states, psychiatric knowledge was largely
limited to the classification of mental disorders by similarity of
symptoms. These classifications often differed markedly from
one author to another and were rarely precise enough to enable

comparative studies to be made. Etiological classifications were rare and explanations of man's behavior—both normal and abnormal—were primitive and animistic. Abnormal behavior was often thought to be caused by a disorder of the bodily humors, by hereditary factors, or by invasion of witches or other ungodly creatures. The explanations varied according to the prevailing theological or philosophical conceptions of man. In later centuries scientific considerations began to influence such theories, but the most widespread interpretations were teleological and assumed to represent some expression of God's will and design. The therapy for these disorders reflected these views and consideration for the individual's feelings. At times the treatment was brutal and destructive; later on it became less punitive, and more compassionate measures—such as rest, occupational and recreational therapies, as well as exhortative and interpretive approaches—were initiated.

Freud, who grew up in the late 19th and early 20th centuries, assimilated and reflected all the prevailing sociological and scientific thinking. Consequently his theories were heavily influenced by the mechanical approach of physics and the instinct theories in biology. Energy as a mechanical force dominated the physiological sciences and the medical sciences were deeply involved in discoveries of the etiology of a wide variety of physical diseases. That Freud's theories were couched in the language of energy (libido) and mechanics (cathexis, countercathexis, repression, etc.) as well as in instinctual notions of human motivation is only natural. The sexual nature of libido became a prime issue in his theoretical formulations, even though his final instinct theory involved the Eros-Thanatos dualism. Freud endeavored to distinguish libido from adult sexual activity; however, he was never fully successful in this area, so that even today the distinctions are blurred or disregarded by many of the most sophisticated psychoanalytic theorists and therapists. As this matter bears on the etiology of obsessive-compulsive behavior I want to examine it briefly.

Although it is clear to all that the child, for example, cannot conceptualize adult sex behavior, it is stated that the Oedipal problems grow out of sexual interest toward the parent of the opposite sex, and in boys that this causes fear of castration. This implies that some knowledge of the sexual function of the genital exists in the child, who until now has been aware only of its urinary function. We must then either assume some Lamarckian inheritance regarding the genital apparatus or concede that a great deal of confusion, extrapolation, and fuzzy thinking surrounds the libido theory. This confusion has particular significance to a theory of obsessive-compulsive behavior when it is postulated that the obsessive mechanism is a defense against sexual or aggressive impulses.

For the longest time man's behavior was considered to be directed by God's will and part of man's nature. Animal behavior was also considered to be the result of God's will, and it was thought to be performed through inborn instinctual patterns of behavior. While man possessed a will and was capable of exercising choice, it was assumed that he also functioned through an elaborate set of instinctual patterns. Freud used instinct as an explanation for man's motivated behavior, behavior that was designed to fulfill many of his innermost needs. Thus in socialization, man was of necessity forced to restrain and control much of his "natural" behavior because his attempts to fulfill his instinctual needs could endanger himself and others. In an oversimplified way, the defenses—which are patterned activities designed to achieve this purpose—constitute the essence of neurosis or psychosis.

The problem of controlling the instincts (sex and aggression) which are pressing for fulfillment constitutes the core of the neuroses and is particularly evident in obsessive-compulsive behavior. Freud, in adopting an instinct psychology, seemed able to comprehend large areas of human activity (both normal and abnormal) which were previously completely unintelligible. He could understand both the purpose and significance of a piece of behavior and develop a motivational psychology of human behavior.

Motivation involves the understanding of behavior in either its short- or long-range goal of fulfilling some need of the organism. Such behavior is neither random nor purposeless; it derives from particular needs or interests of the organism. These needs can often be identified without difficulty even though long-range goals are at times difficult to unravel—both for the individual himself and for the onlooker. Except in special circumstances human behavior has some goal toward which the individual moves with some efficiency or else is interrupted and deviated by a variety of factors. Man's needs differ at various periods of his own development as well as in different sociological circumstances. Freud emphasized the biological needs (instincts) of man while later theorists—such as Horney, Alexander, Sullivan, and others—emphasized man's cultural needs.

A significant advance in the understanding of animal and human behavior was the introduction of the concept of *adaptation*. While this notion was implicit in many of Freud's ideas, the recognition of the role of culture in personality development required the incorporation of the idea of adaptation in theories of personality. Defenses such as rationalization, sublimation, reaction formation, and projection not only were devices to deal with the pressures of instinctual demands but also were some ways of functioning in the face of pressing anxieties. They prevented serious personality disorganization and disintegration and allowed the individual to cope with his anxieties in an adaptive fashion. While in the long run such measures were maladaptive and resulted in neuroses or psychoses, the immediate effect was to prevent disruption of the functioning organism. In this way the concept of adaptation enhanced and broadened motivational concepts even while the psychological theories were instinct-oriented.

While some personality theorists are still reluctant to utilize adaptational frameworks, the group of psychoanalysts called ego psychologists, cultural psychoanalysts, or post-Freudian psychoanalysts has adopted a motivational-adaptational view of human behavior. Man is viewed as an animal who has largely abandoned his instincts in his capacity to learn to cope with internal and external demands. The ego as it confronts the culture has become the main object of study. Thus all aspects of the culture—social, economic, and political—have come within the purview of the behavioral scientist. While an individual needs to deal with his inner biological demands, he must also adapt and adjust to his culture and its idiosyncratic value systems, ideals, goals, demands, and expectations. These needs have differed at various times just as the biological demands differ at particular chronological epochs in an individual's own development. Regardless of one's convictions about the role of instinct in human development, recognition of the effects of the environment in which it must unfold is essential to any comprehensive theory of human development.

The concept of adaptation filled a large gap in understanding the function of a particular piece of behavior in the total economy of the individual. It is possible to recognize that many devices, techniques, and maneuvers (both physiological and psychological) are moves to *defend*—or to protect or overcome dangers or threats of danger to the existence of the individual. They modify the behavior of the organism in the direction of adapting to the situation without succumbing to it. Some of these activities are simple and straightforward; they meet the threat directly in an effort to deal with it. Generally they are more subtle, less specific, and ultimately symbolized, partial solutions which we call neuroses. These techniques are the result of a long, evolutionary process, and the particular pattern of adaptation an individual adopts is based on many unknown factors.

As man evolved beyond the pressure for survival to higher levels of functioning, the dangers to his existence became more subtle and less involved with simple physiological necessities. Ultimately man was no longer exclusively or predominantly occupied with fulfilling his basic survival needs (except as this still exists in underdeveloped areas of the world). These challenges have been largely overcome by man's intelligence in providing ways to increase and sustain his physiological requirements.

Once basic physiological needs are provided for, man is

then confronted with needs that are specifically human and which grow out of his emergence from his animal existence. These needs are the result of man's capacity for self-consciousness and his ability to project himself into the future and recognize his limited powers and capacities as well as his ultimate demise. As a result of these developments, security as a psychological issue becomes a prime need and a major motivating force in human behavior. Man's security needs derive from his awareness of his separateness and his need for human interaction. Feelings of isolation and imposed or imagined threats to his feeling acceptable as a person stimulate a specifically human reaction which is called anxiety. In a greater or lesser degree this response is familiar to every human being; it has its origin in infancy as a consequence of the infant's need for contact and tenderness as well as food and shelter. While generally speaking the infant's physiological and psychological needs are automatically supplied by the environment, anxiety will nevertheless be experienced because fulfillment cannot be indefinitely guaranteed. However, unless the infancy is a particularly stressful one, the role of anxiety in human development becomes more prominent during childhood and in the juvenile years. Being acceptable becomes a more significant concern for the juvenile, and a great deal of activity occurs, the purpose of which is designed to avoid, prevent, or overcome anxiety. Anxiety is a most painful and distressing feeling, and it must be dealt with. In addition to the physiological reactions of sweating, tachycardia, palpitation, breathlessness, etc., there is the overwhelming distress caused by a feeling of impending doom and destruction—accompanied by agitation and restlessness. Such a state can be tolerated only for short periods of time or panic supervenes. Anxiety cannot be dealt with directly, since the sources are usually unknown. The individual therefore develops a number of psychological responses (defenses) to deflect, diminish, or remove the anxiety. The obsessional defense is particularly useful and is thus widely used. Since the anxiety reaction is ultimately caused by some human incapacity, the obsessional defense that attempts to create an illusion of power and control may temporarily dissipate the anxiety. As will be shown, this defense is especially suited to dealing with man's feeling of power-lessness, which is a realistic appraisal that can leave him feeling threatened both by nature and by other humans. If he cannot accept the realities of his limited powers and capacities he will feel endangered in a world which he cannot control. The obsessional defense is an adaptative device to deal with such feelings, and to the extent that some of it is used by all mankind, the defense is universal. When the anxieties and feelings of power-lessness are minimal the obsessional defenses are minimal. As the anxieties increase, the need for greater defenses becomes more insistent and the obsessional defenses become more severe—sometimes overshadowing all other activities of the individual.

OBSESSIVE-COMPULSIVE NEUROSIS

The term "obsessive-compulsive" neurosis refers to a wide variety of phenomena which may be manifested at any time in a person's life. It refers to thoughts, feelings, ideas, and impulses which an individual cannot dispel in spite of an inner desire to do so. The compelling nature of the activity—despite the fact that it may be illogical, undesirable, and unnecessary—is the central issue. Generally such thoughts or feelings are alien to the individual's usual attitudes and are experienced as being somewhat strange, even outrageous, sometimes disgusting, and at times, frightening. Their presence is embarrassing and quite distressing. It is an intriguing development—particularly in the face of current notions of free will and freedom of choice—because in spite of all the wishes, desires, and active opposition of the person, he is forced by some internal pressure to concern himself with a variety of experiences which may be distasteful or frightening.

OBSESSIVE-COMPULSIVE DYNAMISM

Several elements are invariably present and constitute the obsessive-compulsive dynamism. These include:

1) Behavior or thought which persists beyond the need for and/or in spite of voluntary action;

2) the presence of anxiety and somatic distress because of the ego-alien nature of such thoughts; and

3) insight into the illogical and unreasonable nature of the thought or action, which does not alter the behavior.

The obsession is a persistent, ritualized thought pattern, while the compulsion is a persistent ritualized behavior pattern. These elements are invariably present or involved when the thought or action patterns have become ritualized.

The obsessive dynamism can be identified in the personality structure prior to the presence of noticeable ritualized behavior. Such character structures were described by Freud as orderly, stubborn, and parsimonious; others have described them as obstinate, orderly, perfectionistic and punctual, meticulous, parsimonious, and frugal, and being inclined to intellectualism and hair-splitting discussion. Janet described such people as rigid, inflexible, and lacking in adaptability, as being overly conscientious, loving order and discipline, and being persistent even in the face of undue obstacles. They are generally dependable, reliable, and have high standards and high ethical values. They are practical, precise, and scrupulous in their moral requirements. Under conditions of stress or extreme demands these personality characteristics may congeal into symptomatic behavior which will then be ritualized. (The broad obsessional spectrum will be discussed in greater detail in Chapter 5.)

When present, the rituals are dramatic and pathognomonic. The combination of character traits described above is also easily identified. As the purpose and adaptive functions of the variety of personality traits as well as the ritual are better understood, it will be seen that they all subserve the need of achieving control of oneself and the environment.

It was evident to many people long before Freud that such bizarre behavior has great meaning to the person. In more recent years the adaptive value of such behavior has come to be recognized. It has become obvious that the insistent, preoccupying thoughts which cannot be eliminated so fill the attention of the individual that it is scarcely possible for any other thought process to take place. In this way the obsessive thought serves the purpose of distracting attention away from a more significant and possibly more distressing one. This is more easily understood when the obsessive thought is a pointless rumination or an endless speculation about philosophical or religious matters. The distracting or controlling function of such a thought is more difficult to recognize when the thought itself is extremely upsetting and disturbing. Such obsessive thoughts may center around aggressive wishes against significant people, or blasphemous or morally repugnant ideas which cannot be eliminated from one's mind. In either case, the obsessive preoccupation may be total and claim the individual's entire interest, thus preventing any other thought processes. The sudden appearance of highly repugnant thoughts is so bizarre and alien to the person's manifest personality that it immediately distracts him from anything else that might be going on at the time. The occurrence of such fantastic intrusions has provided considerable support for the concept of an unconscious and the notion that ideas and feelings which are outside of immediate awareness can nevertheless significantly influence behavior. Intrusive thoughts which involve screaming obscene words at inappropriate times or places suggest that the individual wants to become the focus of public attention. It seems to contradict the notion that the obsessive thought is designed to distract the individual from public notice and crucial concerns. However, the same basic process is operative when, regardless of how extreme or revolting an obsessive thought might be to the individual, it is still much less distressing than the idea which it is covering up. Freud called this process *displacement* and assumed that the obsessive symptom was always distracting the individual from essential concerns. However, these preoccupying thoughts and ruminations are often the very essence of the person's concerns. Ruminations about death, philosophical and moral issues, or hypochondriacal preoccupations about one's health are attempts to control one's destiny and to guarantee one's future.

It seems to me that it is the need for total control which more accurately describes the entire range of obsessive activity, rather than the simple technique of displacement.

Freud's explanation of the obsessive-compulsive behavior pattern was most illuminating. He emphasized the meaning of symbols in their function of dealing with hostile and unacceptable sexual feelings. He related the mechanism to rebellious actions in overdeveloped super-egos. According to Freud the symptom originated during the anal-erotic period of psychosexual development and was therefore directly related to bowel-training experiences. Sandor Rado put more emphasis on the repressed rage and the adaptive purpose of the symptom in attempting to counteract and undo the repressed rage.

The symptoms oscillate between rage and atonement, which is often expressed in magical terms. Karen Horney and Harry Stack Sullivan placed more emphasis on the attempts to overcome feelings of helplessness and insecurity. More recent theorists, such as Ernest Gebstattel, view the symbols in terms of distorted concepts of time and space, death and existence. Erwin Strauss sees the obsessive mechanism as a technique for dealing with feelings of decay and disgust.

Freud's view of the essential nature of the obsessive-compulsive disorder as relating to toilet training has influenced a large number of behavioral scientists. It involves the notion of a child's battling with his parents against the necessity for withholding his urine and feces until the proper time and place. If the parents' efforts are begun too early and are too extreme, the child may respond with hostile feelings and active rebellion that may be dealt with by obsessive mechanisms. Freud contended that such a development accounted for the widespread presence of obsessive behavior patterns in childhood, which may be manifested in an obsessive-compulsive neurosis in later years. There is currently considerable disagreement about Freud's emphasis on the anal-erotic aspects of such formulations. In addition to the conflicting evidence over the bowel-training struggle, there are many obsessives in whom all the elements of control seemingly affect all areas of their living except the anal function. Meyer Gross and Fritz Redlich disagree about the origin of the "battle of the chamber pot." However, the widespread prevalence of obsessive behavior in children can be readily understood as a factor of the child's helplessness and vulnerability and the need for order and control in dealing with insecurities. The child is also engaged in a struggle for self-expression and in maintaining an identity. This struggle takes place on all fronts and in relation to problems of acculturation as well as to toilet training.

While the factors suggested by many theorists can be identified in the obsessive-compulsive mechanism, the overriding purpose of the behavior is to attempt to achieve some security and certainty for the person who feels threatened and insecure in an uncertain world. The possibility of controlling oneself and the forces outside oneself by assuming omniscience and omnipotence can give one a false illusion of certainty. Therefore the main ingredient is one of control. This notion is neither novel nor essentially different from those expressed by previous investigators. Both Freud and Sullivan highlighted this very element. It is only the matter of emphasis which makes this approach a useful one.

Freud saw the symptom as a device for dealing with unacceptable hostile or sexual impulses. He felt that such people control the expression of these impulses by using displacement, condensation, and symbolization as defenses against them. The symptom, he thought, was a compromise of "doing" the forbidden wish and at the same time "undoing" it. However, not only sexual or hostile impulses need to be controlled but also the tender, friendly, or stupid and unworthy thoughts and feelings. In my view, the obsessive-compulsive dynamism is a device for preventing any feeling or thought that might produce shame, loss of pride or status, or a feeling of weakness or deficiency—whether such feelings are hostile, sexual, or otherwise. I see the obsessional maneuver as an adaptive technique to protect the person from the exposure of any thought or feeling that will endanger his physical or psychological existence. This extends Freud's views and does not require the postulate of an instinct theory or libido theory.

Viewing the obsessive-compulsive dynamism in this light will enable one to recognize its function in the normal person as well as in the neurotic or psychotic one. It will also help one to understand the role it plays in compulsive states such as phobias (compulsive avoidance), obesity (compulsive eating), alcoholism (compulsive drinking), kleptomania (compulsive stealing), etc. This view will clarify the relation of obsessions to paranoid states and other delusional systems in which stereotyped and rigid ways of perceiving the world are the essential issues.

CHAPTER 2

The Obsessive Style

The human infant arrives in a state of absolute helplessness and total dependence upon his environment. Although his capacities to function independently enlarge as he matures physically and psychologically, he is never in full control of the forces which act upon him from the inside or the outside. Some of his physiological functions are autonomic and thus totally beyond his control, just as are some of the forces of nature. In order to experience a minimum of security and a measure of certainty, man constructs a number of myths about his powers and skill in influencing these forces. Such techniques have been used since man developed a cortex capable of visualizing his own self. His structuralizing involved attempts to insure order and consistency in his universe and were often unreasonable. As they were rigidly held and had magical connotations, the devices could be called obsessive mechanisms.

In children these techniques consist of magical, repetitive acts which the child feels will prevent dangerous consequences from occurring if the rituals are carried out precisely. In adults such behavior is called superstitious and irrational; the magical quality involved is readily evident. The greater the extent of fear and uncertainty, the more prevalent will be the magical superstitions and rigid rules of behavior designed to control or master these uncertainties. Kurt Goldstein, in his studies of brain-injured people, noted the subjects' attempts at understanding the environment through extreme measures of orderliness and routinized activity.

Obsessional mechanisms are omnipresent, but in some people they will be more pronounced and will characterize the major ways of dealing with their needs, therefore playing an integral part in their personality structure. Such people's behavior will be predictable and consistent in their reactions to various needs and circumstances. Yet, not all the characteristics of the obsessional way of life are present in all obsessional individuals. Nor will these tendencies always be adaptive or constructive. In the obsessive-compulsive neurosis such tendencies become extreme and maladaptive.

The primary dynamism in all instances will be manifested as an attempt to gain control over oneself and one's environment in order to avoid or overcome distressful feelings of helplessness. The concern about the possibility of losing control by being incompetent, insufficiently informed, or unable to reduce the risks of living produces the greatest amounts of anxiety. The realization of one's humanness—with its inherent limitations—is often the basis for considerable anxiety and obsessive attempts at greater control over one's living.

Fear of loss of control is commonly symbolized in the physical sense as losing control by fainting, by resorting to the extremes of shouting and screaming, or by engaging in other undisciplined activities. Phobias often develop around these situations, in which the person fears he will lose control of himself in giddiness, fainting, swaying feelings, collapsing, or possibly dying. The problem of control in the obsessive person is complicated by his tendency to deal in extremes, so that unless he feels he has total control he tends to experience total *lack* of control. He experiences the possibility of loss of control as so painfully humiliating, frightening, and dangerous that phobic avoidances are common. (The relation of phobias to the obsessional states will be described in a later chapter.)

THE NEED FOR OMNISCIENCE

To achieve control over one's living and to guarantee one's existence one must acquire a knowledge of all the possibilities that may occur. This will permit one to anticipate and be prepared for anything confronted in the course of living. In this way the person can control all the factors involved and achieve the most favored outcome. The striving for omniscience through emphasis on intellectuality is an integral part of the obsessive process and is a major goal. The obsessional can be comfortable only when he feels he knows everything or is engaged in the process of trying to know everything. He is convinced not only that this is absolutely necessary but also that often it is possible, even in the face of his intellectual grasp of the impossibility of achieving the goal. He demands of himself that he be capable of anticipating his own reactions and the emotional responses of others by rational and logical means. He requires that he be able to control the uncontrollable. Thus he expects to know how he will be feeling several days hence so that he can plan properly. He expects his decisions or opinions to be acceptable to everyone, even those who disagree with him or do not know him. He expects to know in advance that his plans will be ideal and agreeable to all. Such expectations often serve to immobilize him and to prevent him from making any plans. He rationalizes the immobility by insisting that he wants only to plan most effectively and to suit everyone. He will say, "If it cannot be done perfectly, then why do it at all?" This has a flavor of righteous and conscientious living and is often rewarded with praise and support. The truth, however, is that it is not based on a moral injunction, but on a compelling need to guarantee the outcome of the endeavor—which is hardly ever possible. It is, in fact, compulsive behavior and not simply conscientious and responsible behavior.

When the compulsive is forced to act, he will often refuse to take full responsibility for the consequences, because he was not fully in accord with the plan and therefore should not be held accountable for the outcome. In this way the compulsive justifies any failure of his activities by placing blame on others who forced him to act. This tendency was quite troublesome to a young obsessional who had great difficulty making dates in advance since he was not quite certain how he would feel when the day of the date arrived, or whether he would want to be with that particular girl at the time. He found it virtually impossible to buy theatre tickets in advance, since he could never be sure of what he would feel like doing when that day came or with whom he would like to do it. He maintained that he did not wish to be committed to advance arrangements so that he could feel free to do whatever he wished when he wished to do it. Since the ultimate effect is actually to limit his choice to whatever is available at the last minute, it is clearly a spurious claim. When he was certain of what he wanted to do and whom he wanted to do it with, he would discover that the girl was already committed to a date with someone else or that the theatre tickets were not available. Thus he ended up with the least desirable girl and at the least desirable place, or he spent the evening alone. As his social life began to dwindle, he was forced to make dates in advance. Then he would invariably wish that he had either made a date with someone else; the evening would therefore always end badly and he would conclude that he should not have made the date in advance in the first place.

The inability to relinquish or compromise, or to take a chance, impairs the effectiveness of the person's capacity for full and mature living. Dating becomes a challenge instead of a pleasant, enjoyable experience. The person senses that there is something amiss in the way he organizes his living, but seems able to do very little about it. Instead, he justifies his behavior with intellectual and philosophical rationalizations. He prefers to present a picture of a thoughtful person who examines issues in depth, instead of acknowledging that his demands for omniscience make action and decision difficult.

Excursions Into Philosophy

Philosophizing can often provide the way to avoid action and to forego decision. While it may be a prelude to action, it often becomes a substitute for living rather than a design for better living. It avoids taking sides, which helps to sustain the aura of omniscience.

Philosophizing provided the impetus for the growth of many seminal ideas in the sciences as well as in the arts. Aristotle, Plato, Descartes, Marx, Whitehead, and a host of other intellectual giants broadened the horizons of man in every direction. For the obsessional, however, philosophizing becomes perverted into a justification for inaction and a demonstration of infallibility. The obsessional will become intensely involved in philosophical considerations of abstract justice, "truth," and other issues about which final statements cannot be made. The preoccupation with the most minute elements of experience, when examined in a formal fashion, has been the source of profound advances in man's enlightenment. But such considerations permit the obsessional to make such issues his justification for inaction. His philosophizing is generally directed at distracting and obfuscating rather than focusing and clarifying. He has a tendency to fractionate or dissect every experience with compulsive rigidity, which confuses rather than enlightens. His verbal skills serve mainly to blur understanding.

The obsessional insists upon arriving at ultimate truths in all matters. He claims a purity of intellectual pursuit in which he maintains that unless certainty can be established, final statements must be avoided. This is a defensive device, particularly when the certainty he demands is in areas in which the possibility of it is remote or unattainable and such a search may seriously impair the possibilities for real discovery. Such unrealistic demands are obstacles rather than challenges to uncovering the laws of man or nature.

While the obsessional's philosophizing is sometimes fruitful, most often it leads only to a dead end when it concerns itself with questions which have no meaning or to which there are no real answers. (Speculations about the number of fairies on the head of a pin would provide an example.) In the search for ultimate truths, one may exhibit intellectual integrity, but in the obsessional the rigidity of the search may be disrupting and digressing rather than creative. While he is seemingly pressing for truth in an uncompromising manner, he is more often launched on a rigid, inflexible program without any realistic comprehension of the obstacles that such demands impose on an investigation.

Preoccupation with ultimate and total truths and abstract concepts of justice is often combined with a rigid set of standards. Exaggerated expectations of the behavior of others and supermoralistic requirements of one's own behavior often pose a caricature of human functioning so that the obsessional may insist upon truth under all circumstances—for example, without taking cognizance of the impossibility of establishing such criteria. It becomes truth for truth's sake alone, and not an honest awareness of the benefits to be derived from adhering to the truth. It is a slogan and a defense rather than a recognition of the virtue of integrity in human relationships. This applies also to his expressed goal of knowing all.

For example, the obsessional husband may insist upon telling his wife everything (including his fringe thoughts) about every girl he admires or feels a fleeting interest in. In spite of this, he expects his wife to admire his honesty and not be discomfitted by his disclosures. He expects his wife to support this caricature of honesty; anything else would indicate that he and his wife have a less-than-perfect relationship, since they agreed from the beginning to tell each other everything. Though the obsessive person expects to be rewarded for his confessions, he, in turn, cannot accept or tolerate similar confessions from his mate.

The abstract concepts of honesty, integrity, truth, and intellectual curiosity have compulsive qualities and are often responsible for a great deal of damage in interpersonal relationships. Such a firm position often puts others on the defensive and forces them to justify their own more limited concepts of virtue and openness. It is always simpler to defend an extreme thesis when one refuses to recognize the realistic limitations of it. Virtue is then entirely on one's own side, and total lack of it on the other. The rigidity of the obsessional often poses moralistic problems in this very way. Questions are resolved on the basis of global formulations. Each instance is not judged in its own right and setting. The rigid rules are applied indiscriminately and unselectively, without any qualifying considerations of the particular situation or circumstance. There is no element of choice in deciding the questions individually, but rather a compulsive necessity to behave in rigid, circumscribed and stereotyped ways. What often appears to be a strong, decisive and affirmative action is the product of precisely the opposite—an uncertain, uneasy, wavering indecisiveness that requires rigid and inflexible rules to overcome. Consequently, what may seem to be a positive, affirmative and moral set of values is simply the compulsive's need to appear perfect and omniscient. Such needs are, of course, manifestations of great uneasiness about one's integrity and honesty and serve as a device for diminishing activity. Such a rigid position prevents a decisive response by an automatic reaction which is always on the side of the angels, even when the circumstances may dictate a more human response.

The philosophical acceptance of high moral standards can become a way of avoiding the responsibility for one's behavior. It is as if one's verbalized standards are enough and one need not be concerned about maintaining them in one's actual living. In this regard society often cooperates, so that the admission of sin in a church confessional may be enough expiation for the behavior. Similarly, the magic words "I'm sorry" may be sufficient to absolve one from the consequences of one's behavior. It is small wonder that serious concern about responsibility is lacking in so many people. Such verbalisms are particularly common in obsessional living, in which the lack of true responsibility for behavior is often found. This state of affairs may produce many conflicts with the community, which may not recognize the validity of the expiating formulas.

Behavioral Doubletalk

At times the recognition of limitations or the admission of a deficiency may appear to be an honest confrontation with one's humanness. It may, however, also be a device for claiming exemptions from the consequences of one's behavior. The disarming admission of one's imperfections is a claim for tolerance with regard to an inadequate performance, which further limits the demands to be made of one. In addition, it is further evidence of the obsessional's superiority; he is "big" enough to admit his failings.

The obsessional is a master in this ploy, and the admission of not knowing everything enhances his superiority and confirms his infallibility. He manages the double bind very successfully by being right when he is right and merely human when he is wrong. At the same time he forces others into a double bind of "wrong when they do and wrong when they don't." The double-bind element is widespread in the obsessional's life and is forced onto most people with whom he has to deal. Because of his need to be decisive but never wrong, he is forced to take stands in which whatever he does must be correct. In practice this is very difficult—unless he can force others to approve his behavior no matter what choice is made. While he avoids direct and open negotiations, he demands that the relationship with him be intimate in spite of the absence of intimacy. He generally succeeds in such relationships for varying periods of time when the other person has something to gain from keeping the relationship intact. This is the case with one's wife, husband, friend, or relative, where the need to be considerate, gentle, or tolerant requires a variety of doubletalk that is pervasive even if it is not identified by the participants. In overt or, more commonly, in covert distortions, confusions and evasions of direct contact, the individual gets involved in double binds which may be quite incapacitating. It often becomes an integral part of the obsessional's living and is the inevitable result of trying to achieve opposite goals and objectives, trying to fulfill contradictory needs and desires, and to achieve omniscience.

Rather than face an awareness of the impossibility of being omniscient and acknowledging his human limitations, the obsessional concludes that if only he knew more and tried harder he could achieve these goals. The solution is to become more perfect, and thus even more obsessional. In this respect obsessional living tends to stimulate the need for more obsessional defenses. This becomes one of the major burdens in therapy since the patient hopes to reduce his anxiety by improving his obsessional neurosis instead of abandoning it. The demands for omniscience, available only to the gods, prevent him from enjoying the rewards of limited potentialities that are available to humans. Even with a total understanding of all the relevant factors in an event he cannot take into account accidental circumstances and the indeterminacy which is an inescapable part of our physical universe. Such expectations lead to a futile impasse, and an enormous amount of time and energy is expended in fruitless efforts to overcome such obstacles.

The obsessional attempts to absorb every piece of information in the universe. Nothing seems irrelevant or unrelated to his interest, since every piece of information may have some value on some future occasion. In attempting to absorb it all he succeeds in absorbing less than he is capable of since his activities are laden with tension and uneasiness. Reading a novel or a technical book becomes a challenge and a chore since every detail must be noted regardless of its significance. He does not read to understand the author's point of view or the theme of the book; instead, he reads to memorize every single idea. Therefore it takes him an inordinately long time to read a book, which results in an accumulation of unread books. This happens even when he limits his reading to a specialized area of concern or professional interest. He quickly finds himself with an accumulated pile of books, newspapers, magazines, and clippings which are put aside to be read later. As the unread material accumulates nothing may be discarded for fear something important will be missed. It soon becomes clear that all this accumulation cannot be dealt with and it is then either moved out of sight or dismissed in one grand cleaning gesture. This vicious circle can be interrupted only by a decision to risk losing some potentially significant information by more selective or directed reading. While it is a decision that all of us must make, it is an extremely difficult one for the obsessional. Eventually, circumstances and the sheer accumulation of material forces him to make a decision. His desk is then cleared so that the vicious circle can begin all over again.

The need to know everything often interferes with his valid interest and desire to keep up with developments in his professional areas of interest. An economist who reads extensively could easily be sidetracked by insisting that every phase of human activity is related to economics and therefore should be on his reading list. Meanwhile the literature on economics continues to pile up unread in his library. This may produce a superficial, dilettante involvement in all developments in the arts and sciences and often gives others the impression that he is a profound scholar with a deep knowledge of all fields. While his knowledge may indeed be varied, his erudition is superficial. The intelligence and energy he expends would result in notable achievements if they were channeled and directed to limited areas.

In the search for omniscience there is a singular incapacity to separate the relevant from the irrelevant since everything is considered relevant to the obsessional's global demands. This incapacity serves to impede any progress toward intensive exploration of one particular area. The obsessional is often a scholar of great repute when he manages to establish some boundaries in his work. It is this type of researcher who undertakes the most tedious and rigorous tasks in relatively obscure areas of human concern which may result in significant discoveries. However, these discoveries occur when the research goes beyond the search for data for the personal security of the researcher and aims at an increased control over nature. Even in these circumstances the obsessional's productions differ qualitatively from the explorations of the relatively free and unrestrained researcher who is curious about himself and nature and is also interested in increasing his control over it. Unlike the obsessive, who is *driven* to such activity, the free researcher may be dedicated, but he is motivated more by the pleasure in his adventures than the decrease in anxiety. Even though there are no pure cultures of "free" or "compulsive" scientists or artists, such a distinction does provide some clues about creativity and productivity, which (although they may coexist), are not synonymous. The creativity of a genius need not derive from neurotic sources; more often it arises from curiosity and a capacity for originality and novelty that is anathema to the obsessive person. The difference between the work of the creative person and that of the obsessional is determined by the motive source of the intense and energetic productions of each. In both there is a capacity for tedious, painstaking activity. One functions out of the positive pleasures of the utilization of his skills, while the other is in search of absolutes and perfection in order to achieve security. For both the rewards may be status, recognition, and financial success—but one will be content and contemplative while the other will need constant reassurances. Both kinds of activity may benefit mankind, but the commitment of the noncompulsive person holds greater promise for meaningful discoveries. He concerns himself with transcending the known and exploring the unknown. This activity is not solace seeking, anxiety avoiding, or pushed on by never-ending doubts and the need for certainties. The obsessional's work may actually *provoke* anxiety and may involve matters which have no possibilities of solution.

Parataxic Thinking

The obsessional's striving for omniscience is frequently reflected in a characteristic development that is called "omniscience of thought." It is an aspect of the tendency to overemphasize the rational, gnostic elements in the obsessional's living. In such thinking (which is also operative in some psychotics), one has the conviction that one's thinking is capable of effecting changes in other people as well as on events. When this phenomenon is present the person feels that he may be responsible for some cataclysm or significant event at a great distance because he may have thought about the possibility of its happening. Specifically, even when such a possibility is positively excluded, the person may feel responsible for the death of another simply because he may have wished the other dead at some time. It is an overestimation of his intellectual capacity and its magical possibilities that permits him to confuse thinking with achieving. The grandiosity implicit in such assumptions prevents him from recognizing that thinking is a prelude to action and not synonymous with it. When the failure to distinguish the process of thinking from the act of achieving occurs in the extreme, we have the typical grandiose delusion which occurs in schizophrenia and in the manic-depressive states.

At times the accidental coincidence of an obsessional thought with some event may precipitate a psychosis by confirming the grandiosity about which heretofore the obsessional had no firm convictions. This type of reasoning, which relates cause and effect to the temporal contiguity of events, characterizes a phase of human cognitive development and has been called *parataxic thinking.* It is a normal development which goes beyond the infant's conceptions of cause and effect. It precedes the comprehension of logical relationships between events and their causes. In parataxic thinking, before a youngster comprehends the nature of lightning or the reasons for anger in another person, he attributes the cause to something which may have immediately preceded it. If a mother is angry when her child asks a question the child may assume the mother's anger results from the question instead of from the quarrel which she had with a neighbor a few minutes earlier. In extreme forms parataxic thinking is the dominant cognitive mode of paranoid mechanisms.

It is possible to exert some influence on others by one's thoughts or by gestures (or other actions which are the outgrowth of one's thoughts) when the other person is in close range or is able to perceive these manifestations of one's thinking. However, unless one accepts the possibility of extrasensory perception, it must be assumed that the person who takes responsibility for events beyond the limits of perception, or under circumstances in which thinking can have no effect, is making magical and grandiose assumptions about the power of his thinking.

Obsessional omnipotence of thoughts and the self-fulfilling prophecy of some neurotics seem to have some things in common. However, there are also great differences. Through his grandiosity, the obsessional may assume to be influencing events elsewhere; the person who subtly and "unwittingly" stimulates others to influence the outcome he has already predicted is producing the so-called self-fulfilling prophecy. This refers to a widespread tendency in some neurotics who anticipate that they will be rejected, for example, and who covertly behave toward others in ways guaranteed to produce rejection.

If an accident should befall the victim of an obsessional's hateful feelings, he may assume total guilt for the event. While such guilt may not have achieved delusional proportions—because there is still an awareness of the irrational nature of it—it may still produce a good deal of expiating behavior. The obsessive person is also overwhelmed by feelings of guilt and may assume blame and responsibility for events because he can never really resolve the doubt about the possibility of his being responsible. This factor plays a large role when confessions are made in major criminal cases under circumstances which clearly indicate that the confession is false. Such confessions, which stem from compulsive tendencies, are often accepted by the courts—even though the evidence is far from convincing.

It is curious that the thoughts involved in the omnipotent concerns of the obsessional are almost always unfriendly and malevolent. He is rarely concerned about the favorable or friendly effects which his thoughts have upon others.

The feeling of the omnipotence of one's thought is almost universally present in early childhood and in the juvenile period and is associated with rituals which attempt to undo the possible damage one's thoughts may inflict. Primitive man's conviction of the power of his thoughts is closely related to magical rites and the superstitions that still plague modern man. Magic, as well as many religious practices, is based upon the belief that devotional thinking can produce significant happenings. This is often coupled with ritualistic practices to guarantee the effect of one's thinking.

When bizarre, unconventional, and extreme claims are made about the power of one's thoughts, they become delusional and part of a mental illness. At these times responsibility is assumed for events which often have not taken place, or which occurred accidentally or coincidentally. Hurricanes, epidemics, and even wars can become the sole responsibility of the obsessional. A phobic avoidance of weapons or other destructive implements, for eaxmple, may be the result of an obsessional's fear that his hostile wishes will force him into extreme behavior.

Intrusive "Homosexuality"

Homosexual thoughts often occur as intrusive elements in many obsessional people when there are no behavioral manifestations whatsoever. The person will interpret these fantasies as evidence of latent or repressed homosexual desires. He frequently interprets these intrusions as representing actual wishes rather than as symbolic or metaphorical statements about his weakness or inadequacy. The psychiatrist, too, often falls into this trap. Such thoughts may not necessarily be wishes; they may be defensive devices designed to distract and displace attention from a significant problem. While Freud also noted this factor, many psychiatrists and psychoanalysts tend to apply the oversimplified notion of wishful thinking to all motivated behavior. In so doing, they thereby strengthen an area of doubt in the obsessional about his strength or prowess, or, in the case of a woman, of her femininity. The occurrence of this type of thinking does not support the theory of latent homosexuality. Instead, it emphasizes the tendency of the neurotic as well as the normal person to draw on all conventional attitudes in a manner that reinforces his neurotic system.

It is, in fact, rare indeed to find an obsessional who puts intrusive thoughts into action; such individuals have never had any homosexual interests or inclinations. The intrusive homosexual thoughts may symbolize nonsexual conflicts and concerns regarding competition and fear of one's capacity in nonsexual areas. As suggested above, these thoughts most often represent doubts about one's heterosexual capacities in the face of the obsessional demands that he perform the sex act perfectly every time. These obsessive thoughts are also likely to appear in the male obsessive who may have difficulty in prolonging the sex act and controlling his ejaculation. The expectation of perfect control prevails in the obsessional's sex life as it does everywhere else. Consequently there is no consideration given to the psychological and physiological effects of abstinence, fatigue, or other debilitating conditions which tend to produce rapid ejaculation. The obsessional maintains that the possibility of prolonging intercourse and maintaining an erection is limitless and that failure to do so is the result of weakness and unmanly behavior. One obsessional was determined to produce an orgasm in a woman who had never been able to achieve one. He prolonged intercourse until he was exhausted or until it was physically painful to his partner. In spite of this, he felt that he was a failure and assumed that were he a better man, he would have been successful.

The obsessional demands that he transcend his biological limits and maintain his erection or postpone ejaculation entirely at his will. His inability to do so may produce intrusive doubts about his masculinity. Interpretation of the obsessive concerns about homosexuality in this light is a liberating one in contrast to the unfortunate tendency to view such doubts as evidences of wishful thinking implying homosexual or latent homosexual interest.

Emotional Demands

The overestimation of one's thinking and knowing as a means of controlling oneself and the universe requires rigid control of one's emotions. All emotional responses must be either dampened, restrained, or completely denied. Since he approaches life in an intellectualized fashion, the obsessional tries to appear unmoved by disturbing or rewarding experiences. He tries to examine each situation as a rational event, insisting that only by putting emotional reactions aside can one be fair and accurate. Such an ideal goal, however, is rarely possible—man's emotional responses are mostly autonomic and beyond conscious control. Since intellectual reactions are entirely under control, it is not hard to understand why the obsessional person places such a great emphasis on intellectuality. Yet, he does not always use his intellectual resources to enlighten or clarify his living.

Man's emotional responses are ontogenetically much older and more primitive than his intellectual development. They arise in the midbrain, while the forebrain is the center of intellectual activity. This physiological fact helps us understand a large portion of the obsessional's desire to isolate or eliminate his emotional responses. As he cannot always control his emotions, he may "get involved" or become committed to people or things too strongly to suit his protective needs. He would prefer to eliminate feelings entirely from his life; because he cannot achieve this end, he uses the technique of displacement—which characterizes obsessive behavior.

Displacement refers to the defense process by which strong feelings are attached to less significant or meaningless activities, thereby removing them from significant areas of living. In such circumstances, for example, a strong, unacceptable reaction may be displaced from a parent, child, or close friend onto some food fad, or distant relative, or political ideology. Such displacement is a means of isolating or distorting feelings and may give a bizarre appearance to an obsessional's behavior. He may appear to be uninvolved emotionally with significant people or events while grossly overinvolved with minutiae.

In the obsessional neuroses whatever emotional elements may be present appear to be attached to unessential or irrelevant issues in the person"s life. In this way he is able to avoid a confrontation with his true feelings and become involved in areas of living which he can control, while *appearing* to be un-interested in those areas which he cannot control. He does not accept emotional responses, when they occur, as normal ac-companiments to living. When they do occur they are justi-fied by extensive rationalizations that make them appear to be reasonable and logical.

The efforts at controlling his emotions may result in a paucity of emotional displays, but they cannot eliminate the enormous ground swells of feeling which are stored up. These untapped emotional sources may periodically burst out, either in minor ways such as slips of the tongue, or other parapraxes, or in explosive, major eruptions. At times the obsessional is quite aware of the presence of these underground forces that he keeps under such strict control. He justifies his controlling behavior by pointing to the intensity of these feelings. He insists that he must keep his feelings in check because they are too explosive to be let out. At a certain point this undoubtedly becomes true, since the vicious circle that characterizes neurotic development allows for an accumulation of feelings because of a need to *control* one's feelings. After awhile the accumulation may be great enough so that the expression of such feelings might be excessive even if the stimulus were minimal.

What the obsessional really wishes to avoid, however, is the expression of *any* feelings—tender or hostile. The freer expression of tender feelings might actually stimulate positive responses from others, rather than rejection. For the obsessional such reactions might be more "involving" and thus more dangerous than hostile ones.

It is not the *expression* of feelings that is actually dangerous, but the failure to express them and the tendency to store them up. Emotional expression in general allows for a more direct and responsive reaction from the other person, which then permits a proper and realistic appraisal of one's situation. Like everything else in the obsessional's life, however, the expression of his emotions is also a matter of all-or-none. The middle road, with its possibilities of moderate reactions with moderate responses, appears impossible for him.

Verbal Juggling

Like thoughts, language is a magical tool to influence and control the environment of people as well as things. The power of the verbal gesture, which seemed to be so successful in the early years, is vastly overestimated now. The dramatic power of his earliest verbalizations as a child and their capacity to influence the adult seem to be retained by the obsessional in his need to control others. In addition, the success of the verbal gesture in minimizing punishment and expiating guilt attests to its magical power. Such verbal maneuvers generally have their origins in the childhood era, when speech development takes place. The molding of sounds into speech and comprehensible words is generally met with great enthusiasm and delight by the parents. These early productions greatly influence others, and one begins to note the power of language in interpersonal relationships. The addition of a vocabulary and skill in utilizing words to assuage and control others and the magical formulas of "I'm sorry!" or "I didn't mean it," and "Excuse me!" becomes part of the child's verbal armamentarium, and are magically successful in relieving the child of punishment, guilt, and responsibility for his behavior.

The recital of a formula which conveys remorse, regret, or the desire to change works so well that it subsequently gets automatized and is a substitute for a program of action. Eventually, the formulas may become divorced from action and are pure verbal productions which evoke all the desirable effects without any motor activity. Words and thoughts become obsessional devices, in which their omnipotence becomes a substitute for active and responsible effort. The devices are incorporated into the character structure of the person, who entertains magical expectations of massive achievement and guilt-expiation through rhetoric and verbal production which bypass any need for doing.

Language can also be used to confuse and distort whenever such may be necessary either as a protective or an adaptive measure. One may wish to avoid direct or incriminating statements while appearing to communicate in an intimate framework. The obsessional has developed this capacity into an art. Aside from the exaggerated need to be precise and accurate, the obsessional has an uncanny skill in leading any exchanges into blind alleys, irrelevancies, and often far from the original intent of the communication. There is a tendency toward subtle changes of subject and emphasis on the nonessential, with an involvement in side issues which are generally initiated by anxiety. This verbal juggling seems to occur when the obsessional senses, in the course of the communication, that he is at fault or that his esteem may be lessened. Verbal magic and rituals are therefore very prominent in this disorder.

The obsessional's security gets tied up with his efforts to avoid actual trial and possible failure, which can produce humiliation. One the other hand, he thinks he can achieve great successes through declamation and oratorical promises without actual trial and confrontation. The use of words to escape living and to confuse and obfuscate is an indirect heritage from early years, fortified by the compelling achievements of words in later years. The patient's extensive use of such verbal maneuvers must always be brought to his attention, and he must be helped to see the function which they play in the illness.

In addition to the voluminous verbal outpourings or the change of subject before a point has been established, the obsessional may use autistic symbolism, tonal devices, or the specious requirements of preciseness and accuracy which require so much qualification and detail that the whole point of the communication is overshadowed and lost. The linguistic and rhetorical skill which he develops through the years becomes a prime tool in his encounters with others. He uses it to justify all his excesses and to make his perfectionistic drives seem reasonable and wholesome. The more extreme his position becomes, the more facile are his explanations. It often requires great skill and marked attentiveness and persistence to keep the obsessional's verbal meanderings and rhetorical ploys in some manageable context—which can be most enlightening to the patient when it is demonstrated.

Since the obsessional views most of his activities as a challenge to his omniscience, every encounter is a contest that he must win. This is also true of his verbal exchanges in therapy, which are rarely viewed as simple communications. They are challenges which turn into debates in which the communicative intent is lost in the struggle to prove his omniscience. This becomes a real problem in the therapeutic process if every interpretation, observation, question, or comment is viewed either as criticism or a challenge to the obsessional's omniscience. Since he requires that he already know all, he cannot accept even a valid statement from the therapist without some initial objection or qualification. In this way he proves he cannot be pushed around and that in the long run he does know more than the therapist.

Simply to accept an observation or interpretation without some challenge is viewed as a weakness and a defect. It is an admission of not knowing everything. He develops great skill in taking from others—in the guise of doing it for the other person's sake, or in accepting it as a token of generosity (since he does not really need what he is taking). This device allows him to maintain his perfectionistic state and his grandiosity by proving that he is not unyielding or rigid, but open to new knowledge and new insights.

The precise and exhaustive manner of speaking which characterizes obsessional reporting is another reflection of his personal striving for perfection. His passion for accuracy and completeness is an effort to eliminate all doubts and uncertainties and place him beyond criticism. Therefore his narratives are filled with minutiae and no detail is left out. These tales seldom get to the point without prodding, as fear of being inaccurate or of making an error requires every kind of qualification to cover all contingencies. The narratives frequently become dull and tedious, and often waste a great deal of time—which is also a way of controlling others by forcing their attention and distracting them from essential issues.

While such devices may appear to be a simple matter of a person's inability to be appropriately selective, careful observation will reveal that the insistence on total detail requires great skill and demands high intellectual capacity. It often demands an intricate knowledge of a variety of matters which others often bypass in the interest of time and economy. The passion for detail in speech may reflect itself in a meticulous attention to dress and in other patterns of behavior. It leads to the precise categorizing of ideas and things so that they can be readily available to buttress one's verbal encounters. Thus detail and order facilitate control over one's activities.

DOUBTING, PROCRASTINATION, AND INDECISION

A most effective way of supporting an illusion of infallibility and perfection is to avoid any challenges or tests which might expose one's deficiencies and errors. One can avoid a test or postpone the inevitable awareness of uncertainties through endless procrastination and indecision. When a decision can no longer be postponed, an element of doubt can then be introduced so that one need not be entirely responsible for the consequences of the decision. Such pervasive vacillating and indecision—accompanied by gnawing, inconclusive doubting—characterizes the obsessive state. At one time the disorder was known as *mania de doute* because doubt is often the most pronounced feature in the illness.

Unless one can be absolutely certain about one's choice or decision one stands the risk of being wrong. This, for the obsessional, is synonymous with being held weak, fallible, and defenseless. Until one can make a final, fully completed and perfect product, it is best to keep it from the view of others, lest they see the imperfections. Therefore, examination papers are held onto until the last possible moment in order to make changes, or manuscripts are not submitted until the final deadline date. Such delays are designed to put off the possibility of adverse judgment, but they are rationalized as a desire to do the finest job possible. Once a task is finished or a paper submitted, it is beyond correction and amplification. If completion is postponed until a deadline forces one to turn in a paper, one can rationalize by insisting that if only there were more time, any imperfections could have been corrected. In addition, the experience is used to support and justify more procrastination, as criticism may be the stimulus for considerable anxiety, which, in turn, will require more defensive patterns and more indecisiveness. The issue may be as trivial as a reluctance to make a date with the hairdresser in case something more important turns up. But it is the pervasive quality of this behavior which is so distressing, even in the most well-organized person. The indecisiveness may have disastrous consequences if no action is taken when action is required.

Decisions cannot be postponed indefinitely. Sooner or later one must decide upon a make of car, the brand of a cigarette, or one's career and one's mate—to say nothing of an endless series of trivial decisions in everyday life. Being forced by circumstances to make a choice, the obsessional may deny the deficiencies in it or become a partisan of it. He may behave as though he is entirely disinterested in such trivial matters and consider himself beyond criticism, joining his potential detractors by disparaging the choice he made and thus being unable to enjoy it. On the other hand, his rigid and unreasonable advocacy of his choice makes him incapable of recognizing its real defects and thereby avoiding the same error in the future. Any decision, minor or major, rarely gives him pleasure. It only serves to increase his anxieties and leave him wishing fervently that he could become more perfect.

Doubting, too, plays a role in the procrastinating. When one is forced to make a decision, one can always maintain that since he had doubts about it, he should therefore not be held fully accountable for the decision. Therefore, whatever the decision made, the obsessional feels that perhaps the alternative would have been better. The activity or issue is often lost sight of when the proper outcome becomes far more important than the activity itself. This is particularly noticeable in sports, when the fun of playing takes second place to winning. Instead of being relaxing, the activity is overladen with tension and obsessional safeguards.

Doubting thus becomes a useful device in sustaining one's omniscience by not committing oneself without reservations and thereby risking a failure. By maintaining an atmosphere of doubt one can easily shift sides to come out with the correct position. Therefore, to avoid error, firm decisions should be avoided.

The obsessional's indecisiveness is also supported by an elaborate pseudo-pride in which he views himself as being objective, honest, and wishing only to examine all the issues involved in making a decision. This, of course, can prolong a decision indefinitely. However, the "examination" does not represent a valid quest but rather a compulsive need to avoid commitment and closure. It allows the obsessional to convey an atmosphere of open-minded flexibility in his desire to avoid quick judgments without an adequate exploration of the facts. It soon becomes evident, however, that what appears to be judicious scrutiny is really a compulsive need to keep the lines open for fear of making a decision.

To illustrate: A restaurant menu carries multiple choices and a diner must finally decide upon one item. The anguish of this choice can often be identified in many people who would like to have a sample of everything, or at least more than one or two dishes. The obsessional is particularly distressed by the need to choose. He wants to have both the lobster and the steak, and knows that he cannot order both. Here the issue is not one of making an error but of making the best possible choice. To order one item only to discover that the other is preferable would be a blow to his pride and omniscience. A compulsive eater or obese person may resolve this dilemma by ordering both. The indecisive obsessional, however, will keep on trying to decide until the last possible moment. He will make a choice, perhaps change it, possibly change it a third time. When the waiter departs, the obsessional begins to doubt his choice and wish he could change it. Embarrassment prevents this and when his dinner arrives he will then find reasons for justifying his indecisions, or he may exaggerate the quality of his choice. Either way, he cannot fully enjoy the dinner because he is annoyed over his doubts and procrastinations.

The same considerations apply to the most diverse and significant decisions in his living, sometimes in a more covert fashion. In both the obese compulsive eater or the compulsive drinker (alcoholic), the difficulty of making a choice is exemplified in the "which one" category as well as the "whether or not" category. Choice is impossible and the compulsion is called an addiction.

Doubting, which serves to fortify the indecisiveness, often comes to play a most prominent role and overshadows all other elements in the obsessional's living. At times it may be so severe that the person doubts that he has really taken a breath or performed a task which, in fact, he may have completed only a moment ago. This may lead to the kind of behavior which has come to be the hallmark of compulsive behavior—compulsive hand-washing, a tendency to recheck doors to see that they were locked, and the like.

These well-described phenomena were presumed to be evidence of the person's hostile intentions toward others (e.g., in rechecking the locked door or turning off the gas). The hand-washing compulsion or the need to check up on one's mate was presumed to represent guilt feelings that were being dealt with by expiatory or *undoing* activities. While such factors may be present, it is clear that the element of doubt in these instances may be so pervasive as to cause the activities to be repeated endlessly and often in circumstances in which hostility plays no role whatsoever. The behavior represents an all-pervasive aura of doubt and uncertainty that does not permit the person to have any conviction of having completed a task; the rechecking is an attempt to achieve some degree of certainty about the matter.

This latter explanation clearly accounts for the repetitive, ritualized behavior of a young man who had to review the contents of his pockets repeatedly before leaving for work in order to be certain that he had not left anything behind. He checked his wallet, his pen and pencil, his glasses, his handkerchief, his notebook, and small change and keys. No sooner had he finished his inventory than he would need to recheck it, and then recheck it again before leaving the house, and yet again in the car, and finally upon arriving at the office before he could abandon the review for the rest of the day. There was no element of hostility in this ritual, merely a fear of making a mistake.

Frequently the doubts about all aspects of living, including who one is and what one desires may paralyze all action. If one feels that his behavior, however trivial, may have disastrous consequences, it is understandable why action must be delayed or abandoned. The obsessional remains immobile and passive and abandons all pretense of making choices. He acts only when circumstances force him to, and then he feels the decision was made by default and not by choice. This allows him to disown the action if it is embarrassing to him. He blames fate or the circumstances that have denied him control of the behavior.

Views on Doubting

Freud thought that the obsessional's doubts were extensions of his ambivalence and incapacity to love. He maintained that the obsessive doubts his own capacity to love because of the existence of hateful feelings toward the loved person. These doubts, Freud concluded, then spread to all the obsessional's activities and relationships because ambivalent feelings exist throughout nature. While it is clear that the obsessive person is often incapable of loving another, it is an aspect of his ambivalence and doubting, and not the *result* of it. It is the feeling of danger in committing himself and abandoning doubts about another that prevents the obsessional from falling in love. Being in love means being concerned about the feelings and reactions of another person—who is not entirely under his control. This situation the obsessional has great difficulty in accepting.

In one sense ambivalence is the experience of wanting and not wanting at the same time. After awhile it begins to stimulate doubts and uncertainties about one's integrity and honesty. But it results from the inability to commit oneself, which stimulates further doubts about oneself and others. It becomes a vicious circle which continues to expand unless interrupted by therapy. In the therapeutic process the doubting expresses itself also as an incapacity to love and an avoidance of involvement with the therapist in a warm, tender relationship. Anger, hostility, and unfriendliness are more easily expressed and acknowledged because they encourage distance. Whenever the patient feels some warmth or intimacy for the therapist he will immediately counter it with doubts about its purpose. He derogates it by thinking that the tender feelings must be devices to entrap or deceive the therapist, or else it may get labelled as latent homosexuality by the patient (or therapist). In this way the doubting serves to prevent intimacy instead of being the result of it.

Sullivan viewed obsessional doubting as a response to the need to avoid clarity and understanding. He felt that certainty was a menace to the obsessional in the communicative process. The obsessional needs to distract, confuse, and cloud up communication; he tends to get into a panic when he begins to establish some clear line of understanding or come to a definite point of view. Thus Sullivan assumed that the doubts were designed to obscure issues and to keep the environment at a distance by demanding advice or assistance which usually alienated the other person or set him off at a distance, preventing any real involvement. Doubt does seem to serve this purpose along with others already mentioned. However, the confusion which is created by the doubting is secondary to its role of avoiding error and the recognition of imperfection. To avoid being wrong one must never take a firm stand and must always be ready to take either side.

Commitment also implies assuming some responsibility for the outcome of behavior. When the obsessional hedges on the issue of his responsibility, the wavering also interferes with the maximum success of his endeavors. It often seems that the disregard of the outcome of an activity enhances and improves it by reducing the anxiety connected with it. However, a total lack of concern or involvement in a project will reduce the enthusiasm for the task and thereby impair the performance. It is clear that in terms of performance an uncommitted attitude may be less destructive to the outcome than the tense, preoccupied, anxious activity of the obsessional. In the face of a decision that cannot be avoided, the obsessional may assume the role of a disinterested spectator in order to allow the activity to proceed more effectively. However, he cannot divorce himself completely from the outcome; his obsessional patterns are quickly manifested.

Extent of Doubts

When the doubts begin to reach psychotic proportions the obsessional may become uncertain about whether he has internal organs or whether he really exists, which in turn may produce massive delusions, misidentification, and confusion as to the very existence of people or places. Some schizophrenics' delusional denial of members of their immediate families, geographical and historical landmarks, etc., is also related to the severity of the patients' doubts about themselves and their environment. Therefore they cannot permit any definite opinions or decisions about such matters as long as the doubts persist. Similarly, the nihilistic delusions of the depressed person—in whom we find the denial of the existence of large areas of his universe—are also the result of profound doubting.

The issue of doubting is also reflected in the problem of free will and free choice. While pretending to make a choice, the obsessional is actually being forced by his neurosis to act in the way that he does. Free choice is possible only when one is prepared to accept all the possible results of his decision and abandon doubting as a technique in living. At the outset of therapy the obsessional cannot make a free choice either about getting treatment or the need for change; therefore the therapist cannot require or expect that such a patient be without doubts about his motivation and desire for change—this change can only appear as therapy proceeds.

The patient's rigidity is manifested in his posture and muscular tonus as well as in the persistent, ritualized, inflexible, and single-minded style of thinking and acting. There is no real exchange or response to the ideas of the other person. Whatever concessions or techniques are employed, he expects agreement on his terms alone. He is unable to shift his attention and interest to allow for any change of subject in his conversations. He certainly cannot allow his attention to wander or to permit spontaneous thoughts to occur. His rigidity makes it difficult for him to move; but once in motion in a particular direction, it is difficult to stop or deflect him.

This rigidity or stability of purpose is extremely useful in the performance of tasks which require intense concentration. However, it interferes with originality by avoiding novelty in one's living. If one must focus on facts or intellectual data, he frequently misses the emotional tone or quality of a situation. This is particularly true in interpersonal or social situations when the facts of an event are often subordinate to the nonverbal communication by gesture, glance, and other somewhat covert signals. The rigidities of the obsessional are observable in every aspect of his living since the adherence to prescribed rules or established patterns of behavior provides an inner security.

Such pervasive rigidity seems to be contradicted by the ambivalent attitudes which the obsessional displays. However, he is rigid about his instabilities and thus may resist inflexibly any effort to alter his more extreme ambivalent attitudes.

Ambivalence

Ambivalence is a quality evident in all people. Everyone at one time or another will have mixed and at times opposite feelings toward the same person. In psychiatry, however, the term has taken on a special meaning. It was first used by Bleuler to describe the contradictory feelings noted in schizophrenia, in which the patient exhibited marked fluctuations in his feelings of love and hate, which may coexist in varying proportions toward the same person. Freud, too, was impressed with this phenomenon and explained it on the basis of unconscious feelings which are inconsistent with conscious ones. Freud assumed that when a person outwardly professed love but belied it by his actual behavior (which conveyed hate), his hateful feelings could be unconscious. Freud believed that marked ambivalence was the basis for severe conflict and personality disorganization, as in the neuroses and psychoses.

It is naive and idealistically visionary to conceive of absolute and unconditional feelings of love or trust toward another person in the realistic world of denials, frustrations, limitations, and disappointments. As the infant and child are required to conform to the requirements of the culture in which they live, discipline replaces permissiveness and demands are made of the child which he may not completely accept or enjoy. In addition, he inevitably faces some disappointments, disapprovals, and punishments—as well as rewards, satisfactions, and tenderness—from the significant people in his life. In this way ambiguous and mixed feelings of love, trust, hate, and distrust become tied up with the same person, without necessarily producing conflicts.

The obsessional, however, is unable to tolerate ambiguities and unpredictable responses. He has great difficulty with the ambivalent feelings he recognizes in himself and others. To be certain of how others feel about him, he must either have absolute power over the other or be unaware of the other's negative feelings. He could also be so committed to a relationship of love and trust with another that he might have no doubts about that person's feelings. Since the obsessional has great reluctance to commit himself fully, he finds himself trapped in a contradictory goal of trying to eliminate ambivalence but at the same time maintaining it; this produces great tension in his relations with others. He generally manages this dilemma by having immoderate views about people or things. In this way he may have extreme and absolute feelings but also be able to shift to the opposite extreme—thus managing to maintain ambivalent but absolute attitudes. He may even consider this a virtue and an example of his flexibility. However, it is really a way of not acknowledging ambivalences.

Ordinarily we try to acknowledge and to a certain extent accept the failings and deficiencies in others, particularly in those we love. We may be critical and resentful at times, but we do not reject such persons completely if they should let us down or if they fail to recognize or reciprocate our tender approaches. As long as the over-all feeling is one of positive interest and affection, we are able to accept temporary feelings of disapproval or disappointment toward and from these persons. The obsessional cannot tolerate such uncertainties; he views ambivalent feelings or tolerant attitudes as weak or dishonest. He has contempt for what he calls a compromise with deficiencies and demands of himself that he maintain firm, fixed attitudes without qualifications or reservations. Thus the awareness of ambivalent feelings leaves the obsessional feeling weak and threatened. When he notes such ambivalences his guilt and anxiety are related to the hostile elements in these feelings and to the self-derogatory attitudes which are then stimulated in him.

Freud tended to overemphasize the hostile issues as the focal concern in ambivalence; he believed that the hostile feelings accounted for the guilt and self-derogation which resulted. However, hostility is not the only element which produces guilt; ambivalence in interpersonal relationships is also related to the cultural attitudes about loyalty and dedication toward those who support us as well as one's intolerance toward ambiguities and ambivalence. Freud was greatly influenced by his own cultural background, in which children were expected to behave properly and to respect their parents without any show of defiance or rebellion. Ambivalence was not tolerated and a display of anger or hostility toward parents was quickly followed by stern punishment. However, covert ambivalence flourished while outward demonstrations of unfriendly attitudes were discouraged. Freud was describing a situation which was widely prevalent in the middle and upper classes of some cultural groups. Child-rearing practices and child-parent relationships have, however, been vastly altered in the intervening years. Some cultures have become permissive and have allowed children to express their negative feelings as well as their positive ones toward adults. Mildly hostile gestures have been encouraged in other cultures. At one time permissiveness was presumed to be the basis for later securities, while at another time (and based on later findings) the setting of limits and discipline is presumed to be the basis for developing healthy adults. Cultural practices vary. Demand feeding of infants was followed by more scheduled feedings—and each program was supported by most authoritative statements and held to be the certain road to sound mental growth. The prevailing trend over the past 40 years, however, has been to encourage the child to express his negative feelings toward adults, as it is assumed that such feelings inevitably occur in the course of a child's development and that it will be less damaging for the child to express them than to suppress them.

Certainly when ambivalences are accepted, guilt feelings are lessened. This development not only finds some rationale in present psychological understanding of human behavior but also is in accord with the freedom of expression encouraged in democratic societies. It reflects the notion that love or affection should be earned and not simply expected or demanded by an authoritarian figure who has the physical power to enforce such a demand.

The requirement of total loyalty and devotion and a parental insistence of absolute love and affection can only create conflict and anxiety. This is particularly true when such demands are made by parents in a family situation in which a minimum of tenderness and love is present. It is from such a family background that obsessional patterns are most likely to develop as a means of coping with the ambivalent feelings which inevitably occur. As demands for absolute devotion are most likely to come from parents who are themselves obsessional, it is easy to visualize how, without the need for a constitutional explanation, children become obsessional. Doubts, guilts, and uncertainties stirred up by the child's mixed feelings are often dealt with by denying or being selectively inattentive to one segment of these feelings—giving a spurious notion of resolving the ambivalence. (The process is often called repression.) At other times obsessional rituals and preoccupations are widely used to distract the child from these disturbing ambivalences. If such defenses work, the child may seem to have firm and positive feelings, but he feels divided or at war with himself.

At that time when the child is entirely dependent on adults and is therefore insecure and vulnerable, too rigid demands for control of his behavior (as well as his sphincter) may cause him to develop severe anxieties which he attempts to limit by obsessional ritualistic patterns and rigid standards of perform ance. Compliance is often the price the child must pay to guarantee acceptance and to prevent rejection.

It is small wonder that early childhood is normally "loaded" with obsessional behavior patterns. If the situation is extreme, a neurosis may develop to allow the child to deal with the expectation of complete rejection. The amount of obsessional patterns present in childhood is an index to the degree of struggle of the dependent child in an unreasonably demanding environment. In families in which dissidence is forbidden and perfection is demanded, obsessional rituals and phobias will be more common. If the family situation encourages outspoken feelings and allows for the child's deficiencies, such symptoms may be minimal.

The relationship of obsessional developments to ambivalent attitudes has put the emphasis on the need to control hostility. However, ambivalence goes beyond hostility and may develop out of the discrepancy between the infant's idealized conception of all-giving parents and the parents who demand more controlled and socialized behavior. Ambivalent attitudes occur simultaneously with, and are not the causative agents in, obsessional developments. The inevitable disciplinary measures required in bowel training, achieving cleanliness in eating, dressing oneself, and the like may provide ample opportunities for feelings of anger and disappointment towards the adults who previously were completely permissive and accepting. The same background for the production of obsessional defenses produces ambivalent feelings; the guilt which follows owes not only to the hostile feelings which are felt but also to the inability to fulfill the adult demands and requirements.

In later years, the obsessional's recognition of ambivalent attitudes is looked upon as weakness; he demands positive, "black or white" attitudes on all questions. This applies not only to feelings about people but also to matters of taste or preferences in music, art, etc. Clearly it is not weak or dishonest to suspend judgment or to have mixed feelings on issues wherein absolute determinations cannot be made, as in matters of aesthetic taste. On some occasions it may be the essence of integrity to avoid extreme positions. But the demand for absolutes and certainties does not necessarily imply conviction. The obsessional requirement insists upon absolute judgments when only aesthetic preferences are possible. While the obsessional's directness and unequivocating opinions may convey the impression of honesty and forthrightness, they also convey the picture of an opinionated, rigid individual.

Ambivalence, ambiguity, and uncertainty are unavoidable ingredients in human existence. To function effectively and without undue anxiety one must recognize this existential fact. The obsessional who tries to overcome these issues through perfectionistic and superhuman achievements is doomed to fail.

Much mischief has been produced by the notion that ambivalence involves feelings of love and hate and that the resolution of the ambivalence would result in the cure of many neurotic problems, including the obsessive-compulsive neuroses. Ambivalence is the natural outcome of human development and produces difficulties only when absolute and rigid attitudes are demanded of one. It is then that guilt feelings and feelings of unworthiness are experienced, together with expectations of rebuke and rejection. Therefore these feelings must be kept under control and out of awareness, even though they may represent wholesome and independent responses to people or events.

Closely related to the problem of ambivalence is its opposite—the tendency to think and feel in extremes or to react in an all-or-none manner. As the obsessional is concerned about this tendency, he justifies his demand for absolute control on the basis of preventing these extreme responses from occurring. The exaggerated feelings which he experiences are often the result of his incapacity to allow minimal reactions to be expressed. Since he lives in extremes, his expectation in relinquishing some control is to respond in the extreme, i.e., to feel completely out of control—and this is completely unacceptable to the obsessional (as it is for anyone else). The heart of the matter is whether human reactions and responses need to be "all or none." The obsessional views all situations and experiences only in extremes. Any compromise or acquiescence is viewed as weakness. He despises the indecisiveness in himself and insists that he must always be firm and definite. The pattern seems to derive from the desire to convey a picture of a firm, integrated, and positive person—which the obsessional wants very much to be.

In the atmosphere of all-or-none, tenderness cannot be given in a total sense as it is already viewed as a weakness and as giving in to someone else, which leaves one vulnerable. Like the other characteristics of the obsessional described above, these extremes do not occur all of the time. They are, however, sufficiently present to be consistent elements in the personality structure.

Further Attitudes and Symptoms

Much of the symptomatology of the obsessional state—such as the subject's meticulousness or sloppiness, dependent or independent attitudes, absoluteness or pervasive doubting—is related to the tendency to respond in extremes. Any in-between attitude is viewed as weakness. Being average or ordinary is contemptible, and mediocrity is the disgraceful acceptance of one's limitations. The obsessional therefore sees people as either exceptional or ordinary. There is no room for anything in-between.

When the obsessional is forced by circumstances to recognize his limitations and to acknowledge that he is, after all, a mortal human and not a superman, he may become quite depressed. Why does he react so violently to the notion that he is only human? On one level he does wish to be like everyone else, but on another level he has a need for absolute control and certainty—with guarantees that he be a superman. To him, an ordinary person is weak, helpless, unable to control the universe —someone who is pushed around and forced to yield to the control of others. The obsessional cannot acknowledge the fact that everything is not all black or white and that not everyone is either totally in control or controlled entirely by someone else. Most people function more or less independently while at the same time they are dependent upon others. The obsessional equates normality with stupidity. For him, anything less than perfection is mediocrity, which is intolerable. He cannot recognize that acknowledging one's limitations enables one to achieve realistic goals, while he, on the other hand, with his extreme all-or-none philosophy, may have expansive but impossible goals which he then makes little effort to achieve. His goals usually remain on an idealized and verbalized level, mostly unrealized. His failure to achieve them is often rationalized as caused by the interference from others.

"Mediocre" is the derogatory label he applies to most hardworking, successful (or unsuccessful) people. Some other people are idealized, glamorized, and exaggerated far beyond the reality of the situation. These idealized images can rarely withstand close inspection, and when reality sets in, these persons are the ones who are treated with venom and exceptional bitterness.

To be acknowledged as a leader, beyond fear of danger or criticism, is rarely possible. Yet this is what the obsessional insists upon being, since he feels that some have achieved this (e.g., the President, a king, etc.) and therefore it should be available to him. Accidents of fate, birth, or genius do not exist; for him everything is possible. In spite of these professed beliefs, the obsessional is reluctant to take the initial steps toward or to assume any risks in arriving at these goals. He cannot run for office if there is a danger of defeat. He will not gamble unless all the odds are in his favor. He will buy only two sweepstake tickets—but he will be furious if he loses. While his demands are at one extreme, his willingness to accept the risks and challenges to achieve these goals are at the opposite one.

The problem of extremes characterizes all the neuroses, even though it is particularly noticeable in obsessional states. All neurotic symptoms appear to be exaggerated responses, extreme activities, or overcompensated defensive developments. This is a phenomenon which is not yet clearly understood. The parallel in the external world or in the organisms is that of adaptive techniques' overcoming physical deficiencies. Animals lay millions of eggs to guarantee the survival of some; the plant kingdom abounds with excesses to assure minimal survival. In the same way, the leukocytes respond in excessive amounts to invading organisms as the repair apparatus overacts to insure certain processes. In addition, there are parallels to the all-or-none reaction in the obsessional state that resemble the response of the nerves—which appear to react in this fashion. The tendency to over-react, which is evident in obsessional behavior, is an intrinsic part of the tendency of living matter to approach all dangers and threats as serious, even if they are trivial. The full force of the counterattack or defense may be brought into action to overcome the attack. The obsessional often acts as if he is unable to distinguish the serious from the trivial danger, or else he magnifies all the dangers in order to be invulnerable to any kind of attack.

GRANDIOSITY

A significant outcome of the tendency to deal in extremes is the development of grandiose attitudes toward oneself. This is the obsessional's response to his attempts at omniscience and omnipotence. It is likely that he looks upon himself covertly as a superperson, even while he feels helpless and impotent. Because he sees himself as someone who is striving for perfection, or believes that he has already achieved it, he has a grandiose view of himself. This is not the result of a realistic appraisal of his capacities and capabilities but is an outgrowth of the high standards and impossible demands which he makes upon himself. It is his unwillingness to settle for anything less than the best which makes him feel superior to others and is frequently responsible for arrogant and contemptuous attitudes toward those who will settle for "second best."

In spite of his arrogance and grandiose contempt for others, he feels also that he is inferior to others—and therefore unsafe. As has already been indicated, his perfectionistic demands often result in notable feats of scholarship. His devotion to a task and his desire to know everything frequently result in achievements of great competence. Even under these circumstances, however, he remains dissatisfied and critical of his realistic achievements, which never seem able to satisfy his strivings for absolute perfection. The realistic basis for pride is lost in his own disparagement and disappointment and in his failure to achieve absolute success. This picture presents a difficult therapeutic problem because the obsessional esteem in the patient's neurotic achievements prevents the growth of valid esteem. He tends to belittle his small therapeutic gains and yearns only for superhuman, impossible achievements.

A striking illustration of this situation was that of a highly competent but seriously obsessional physician who became greatly upset when he could not diagnose every disorder that was brought to his attention. While he read all the current literature in his specialty, he was dissatisfied because he could not keep up with all the other specialties as well. The need for absolute and certain diagnoses led him to prescribe costly and often unnecessary laboratory studies to eliminate even the slight possibility of the most remote disorders. He could never accept obvious evidence for simple and common diseases, but felt impelled to rule out all possibilities of exotic and rare diseases. In addition, he felt that he should be expert in all the subspecialities, and would refer patients to other specialists only with the greatest reluctance and with feelings of failure.

The doctor's patients would occasionally interpret his meticulous and exhaustive studies as evidence of concern, interest, and great competence. More often, however, other interpretations were made that were less flattering as patients would note that much of his uneasiness seemed stimulated by his doubts and requirements for perfection. They noted his lack of concern for the costs involved in the tests prescribed or for the discomfort of the extensive studies which he ordered. Most of his patients became critical of his obsessive indecision and pervasive doubts in spite of the enormous amounts of time and devotion which he gave to each patient. Secretly, he felt that he was the best, most careful doctor in the world. He thought of himself as a twentieth-century William Osler and secretly claimed that if he were given enough time he could diagnose every human disorder that appeared before him. Consequently, if a patient became critical or dissatisfied he was deeply offended and very surprised. He could not entertain the slightest possibility that his claims were extreme or that his conception of himself was grandiose. Instead, he prided himself on being precise and concerned only with the patient's welfare. He could never admit to an error in diagnosis, or that an incomplete diagnosis was the result of his deficiency or incomplete knowledge of the voluminous detail of the medical sciences. Instead, he always blamed the pressure of circumstances which did not permit him enough time—or the technical deficiencies of the laboratory or the demands of the society for quick patient turnover. He had to insist on repeated tests with the feeling that ultimately the answer would turn up. If he discovered a lesion, particularly a potentially cancerous growth, he felt guilty for not having discovered it earlier, regardless of when it might have occurred. The possibility that the lesion had not existed at the prior examination never relieved him of the obsessional demand that he should have somehow predicted or anticipated the lesion. Such episodes would reinforce his overzealousness. Instead of acknowledging man's inability to anticipate or predict everything, he refused to make final statements on the possibility of the presence of a lesion, as such would indicate that it just might have been present in previous examinations. This increased his indecisiveness and doubting.

Another example of this type of grandiosity was manifested by a man who was quite annoyed with his wife when she refused to countenance his open liaison with another woman. He could not understand her resistance to inviting this woman to live with them. He felt that if his wife really loved him she would readily support such an arrangement, since he really needed both women and felt that he was entitled to it because he was such a valuable member of mankind that ordinary rules should not apply to him. After his wife obtained a divorce he offered her the same arrangement in his new household. He could not see that his demand was grandiose and egocentric.

For the obsessional, always being in the right (exempt from criticism) is not a grandiose claim. It appears to be a reasonable expectation of someone who deserves it. He feels that his high ideals and exceptional standards merit only the highest rewards. Therefore, he should be free from criticism because he tries to be perfect—and he should not be criticized if he fails to attain perfection. Since this does not ordinarily occur, a great deal of resentment and grievance is felt by the obsessional. This pattern of grandiose development with its claims for exemption from human responsibility is the cause for many complications that occur in compulsive states—such as obesity, addictions, and kleptomania.

It is inevitable that the grandiosity of the obsessional will be challenged directly or indirectly by the notable successes and achievements of others in comparable age groups. This is particularly upsetting to the obsessional, as he can no longer deny such achievements. He will attribute others' successes to their being richer, more opportunistic than he, without his integrity, etc.

He will maintain that he could have done as well if he had really wanted to, or if he had sacrificed his principles. More and more rationalizations are required as time goes by, as are more obsessional symptoms to overcome the realistic differences. The illusion of grandiosity is not maintained by realistic achievement but by a denial of the realistic limitations.

RITUALS

The obsessional's need for absolute control requires an omniscience and omnipotence impossible to achieve. Reality constantly intrudes itself into his life in spite of all his efforts to deny it. Therefore he may call upon superhuman sources of strength and power in order to overcome any human limitations. The efficacy of magic is presumed to be enhanced by a ritualistic performance which is precisely defined by the magic maker and passed on to future generations. The belief in magic and the possibility of influencing others through verbal formulae or ritualistic behavior has been practiced since the beginning of man. While magic was more prominent in the daily routine of primitive man, it still plays a role in the activities of modern man—either in his religious practices, in obsessional activities, or both. It was more prevalent when man's control over nature was severely limited by his lack of comprehension and knowledge; his dependence upon magic was great and it played an intrinsic role in his culture. As man's knowledge increased, his need for magic in its primitive forms decreased and it was manifested in more artful and sophisticated ways. However, in times of crisis and stress it may still dominate an individual's behavior. This is what takes place in a subtle and symbolic way in the obsessional mechanisms. Rituals and the belief and dependence on magic are common accompaniments of obsessive processes and may be the most prominent elements in the obsessional neurosis. The ritual is an attempt to control the individual's behavior by focusing his attention on the ritual, thereby distracting interest away from other matters. In addition, it may be a symbolic performance in which the individual controls those elements which he feels may go out of control.

In a more general sense the ritual is an attempt to gain some control over a superhuman agent by a direct appeal in which the action is presumed to be satisfying some desire of a god. It may be simply expiatory or supplicatory when repetitive formulae or placating sacrifices will influence the gods in one's behalf to perform the action desired. This is the essence of any ritual as it is performed by the most primitive or the most sophisticated cultures.

Primitive man, when exposed to real threats to his physical existence, had few resources to deal with these dangers. The rituals were as varied as the dangers that man faced, and there were malevolent as well as benevolent powers to appeal to. The rituals developed from the needs of a group, which were largely determined by geographical factors. The advent of monotheism simplified ritualistic practices by focusing on one godhead, although patron saints for particular needs were retained. Some rituals could be carried out by the individual himself, while others required the intercession of an especially gifted holy man who would make contact that ordinary mortals presumably could not. Some rituals have remained unchanged as they passed through primitive magic, paganism, polytheism, monotheism, and throughout the developments in science. Others became more refined and rationalized. The scientific advances which increased man's understanding of nature have been accompanied by a decrease in the use of rituals and magic. The overwhelming influence of religious systems of all kinds has diminished as man's grasp of the world and of himself has increased.

Yet rituals still persist in many disguised forms even today (and in all superstitious beliefs) because man is still unable to control nature—nor is his knowledge complete. Despite all the monumental advances in science and technology, man is still handicapped in his control of energy sources and the cataclysms of nature. The knowledge of his physiology and the functioning of his inner world is still in a primitive state. Because of the finiteness of his existence, both in longevity and cerebral capacity, it is likely that he will never reach a point where he can exercise total control over himself or the universe. It is therefore not surprising that he continues to have large numbers of ritualistic practices and magical assumptions in areas such as the possibility of life after death, or the existence of heaven, or control over all disease, or life on other planets, etc. As knowledge expands, science replaces ritual. Cloud seeding begins to replace the rain dance. However, in areas totally beyond man's control only the acceptance of his limitations will permit him to abandon superstition and ritual. It is in this connection that the relationship of ritual to obsessional behavior becomes evident. The persistence of rituals in spite of man's scientific advances owes largely to man's insecurity and uncertainty, which still prevails. Reason, logic, and knowledge are still not sufficiently developed to permit man to function comfortably in the face of human deficiencies; thus ritual in the obsessional mechanism is pervasive.

Forms and Meanings

Obsessional rituals are as variable as the elaboration of man's imagination. However, they usually have some relevance to the particular needs of the individual and may frequently be symbolic dramatizations of the particular problems the individual is attempting to resolve. Like religious rituals, they consist of a series of repetitive activities which must be precisely performed; otherwise anxiety ensues. The individual may have some rational explanation of his behavior, or else he may be aware of the nonsensical nature of the behavior and yet be unable to stop it. It cannot be terminated by reasoning or persuasion as its origin is not intellectual and therefore cannot be altered by "clear thinking." While the ritual may be meaningless intellectually, its function as an agent of control has emotional roots and can be understood only in these terms.

At times the meaning of the ritual may be obvious and its adaptive purpose clear. If one has obsessional preoccupations about murder or destruction, the ceremonious avoidance of knives or rituals involving measures for the control of one's anger are easily understood. On the other hand, some rituals are incomprehensible in their entirety. For example, a young man was compelled to walk 12 paces north and 5 paces east ten times while repeating the word "aroribus."

Doubting is an integral part of many rituals. For instance, the obsessional must go back and try the door handle to make certain it is really closed, or recheck the gas-stove jets to make sure they are turned off, or rewash his hands to guarantee their cleanliness. These are not illustrations or admissions of human frailty, but compulsive efforts at perfection. Originally, Freud utilized such examples to emphasize the underlying hostility or the aggressive impulses which lay behind the obsessional ritual. He felt the ritual implied that the obsessional covertly wished to burn his house down and was overtly trying to avoid this by rechecking the door or the gas range. The obsessional's inclinations toward violence needed to be checked by his avoidance of knives or other dangerous instruments. However, many rituals have nothing to do with violence or sex. With the young man who checked and rechecked his pockets' contents, the ritual was a matter of control and certainty. Such rituals are more common in the obsessional, although they are not so dramatic as those which are clearly involved with the avoidance or control of violent or sexual impulses. Rechecking is a way of overcoming the doubts and uncertainties about an action.

Ordinarily a person washes his hands with the expectation that he will do a reasonably good job at it. Not so the obsessional. He might express it as follows: "If I wash again, I will reduce the risk of germs, so washing again and again will reduce the risks altogether. But two hours of handwashing is all I can spare, since I must also dress perfectly, eat perfectly, etc., which will make further washing impossible." The termination of these rituals is often the result of outside pressures, since the doubting which produces the symptom prevents a firm decision to terminate it. At times, the rituals become so extensive that they exclude all other activities; ultimately the routine demands of living require their termination. The ritual is designed to achieve certainty, and the fact that this is impossible to achieve is the sad fact of the obsessional illness.

One type of ritual has attracted a great deal of attention from psychiatrists for many years: the ritualized avoidance reactions we call phobias. They enable a person to control his living to the extent that he eliminates the possibility of anxiety which may occur in certain situations in which he feels vulnerable, and in which he may lose control. In this way the phobia is precisely the same as other rituals.

Rituals are often dramatic and striking elements in the obsessive-compulsive neurosis, particularly when they are bizarre and carried out in public. However, rituals of all sorts play a significant role in everyone's life in that they are economical ways of managing one's life. Each of us has a particular way of going to bed, a particular routine for the morning ablutions, and a wide variety of stereotyped and repetitive ways of performing many routine activities. Such "rituals" do not necessarily involve the avoidance of anxiety—except as they routinize the regular activities of one's existence, avoiding the requirements of choice or decision. They are analogous to reflex action, except that they are learned and are capable of modification when necessary. It is this element which distinguishes such rituals from obsessional rituals which are required to cope with potential dangers, and if changed or interrupted, will result in severe anxiety. The impeded or interrupted obsessional ritual will cause feelings of restlessness, uneasiness, and apprehensiveness in the neurotic. It is the reaction which accompanies the feeling that one may get out of control. Thus if the danger of losing control is experienced as very great, then the reaction to interrupting the ritual may be overwhelming.

The compulsive ritual which consists of a series of motor acts is identical to the relentless repetitive and persistent thoughts of the obsessive process. It also *controls* by taking over the central interest of the individual, thereby diverting his attention. It is a very successful device and can be so oppressive at times in its demand for attention that the individual is unable to do anything else. At other times it may be present even though the person is actually performing other activities that require his interest. At such times he is obviously unable to give his full attention to the matter at hand.

Freud assumed that every ritual was accompanied by an "undoing" because the obsessional's ambivalence was involved. Freud described it as "a kind of negative magic . . . in which the individual's second act abrogates or nullifies the first in such a manner that it is as though neither had taken place whereas in reality both have done so." (*The Problem of Anxiety*, W. W. Norton, 1936, p. 33) The undoing not only preserves the ambivalence but is also an expiating activity. However, this interpretation of Freud stems from his notion that obsessional rituals develop from aggressive or sexual impulses. Thus in his examples the undoing can be an effort to restore the balance. If, however, the ritual is the result of a need to deal with weakness or an illusion of helplessness, an appeal for help to a superior being may be experienced as humiliating for someone who must always be strong and powerful. The undoing element may therefore deny the weakness in the appeal and restore the feeling of omniscience and omnipotence. The extent of the "undoing" element in the ritual will be determined by the obsessional's need to maintain face and the illusion of strength in spite of his illness. Some are unwilling to face any awareness of their helplessness if the attitude of the culture toward weakness is highly condemnatory and such ritualistic appeals for help may require an "undoing" element. On the other hand, the ritual itself may be viewed as an aspect of the obsessional's power rather than as a weakness.

The "undoing" is also an aspect of the obsessional's doubting tendency—even in this instance he cannot fully commit himself to the ritual. The "undoing" may need to be part of the ritual as an expression of the uncertainty of one's use of it. "Undoing," however, is not necessarily a part of every ritual, nor does it seem to be an essential element in it.

CHAPTER 3

Commitment, Sex and Marriage

The obsessional's attempts to be in complete control of himself and others is endangered by his dependency needs. He would prefer to achieve an independence that would free him entirely from needs which he cannot fulfill for himself. However, totally independent living in a physical and psychic sense is an impossibility for man.

Dependency is a natural state which characterizes both living and nonliving matter; it is an essential quality in man's existence. Whether a person's relationships are parasitic, cooperative, or collaborative, he depends on other humans as well as on nature. Yet he must balance his dependency with a measure of self-sufficiency and a capacity for independent behavior which allows him to be creatively adaptive.

At times, because of some physiological defect or psychological "warp," an individual has a greater-than-normal need of others and is more dependent upon them. When this occurs, a great deal of trust must be present in a relationship or else security is decreased instead of increased. Unless one can be certain that his dependent needs do not stimulate resentment in others there is always the danger of feeling rejected or abandoned. Such doubts can sometimes be assuaged if one is in a position of strength and able to demand absolute loyalty from the person upon whom he is dependent. Generally, however, the dependent person is in doubt about his status and position. To be committed always means to abandon total independence for mutual interdependency.

Being dependent is interpreted by the obsessional as being out of control and under the influence and control of someone else. This extends not only to his intimates, upon whom he can feel almost comfortably dependent, but also to inanimate objects such as an automobile or a TV set. He may refuse to acknowledge his dependency upon the forces of nature and react with anger, frustration, or exaggerated feelings of helplessness when, for example, changes in the weather interfere with his plans. At such times he is forced to acknowledge his dependency and he may be forced to alter his plans and his freedom of action. If such circumstances continue for a long period of time a breakdown may occur in his obsessional adjustment. This may be the case when a hitherto integrated obsessional pattern begins to crumble with the birth of a child, which forces a limitation on the freedom of action of the parents.

The most striking and debilitating difficulties occur when the obsessional is unwilling to acknowledge his dependency on the proper functioning of his body and its limitations. He resents the fact that his energies are limited or that he cannot engage in exercise or play without some rest even while he is intellectually aware of the limitation. He may resist going to sleep or taking a rest; to do this would be to acknowledge the limitations of his physiology and would also mean giving up control. For this reason many obsessionals have difficulty in falling asleep, though they usually sleep soundly once they do.

They also resent having to limit their eating and drinking,

and become furious if their excessive indulgence produces some gastric distress. They may refuse to wear a coat or rubbers; weather should not determine their actions. They make impossible demands on other people as well as on their material possessions. Cars should not break down, airline schedules should not be altered, gadgets should always function perfectly. The obsessional is angered when such events occur and feels them to be impositions on him. He cannot accept accidental events as part of human existence; he is resentful of them. He may be even more incensed at his inability to control or prevent these accidental occurrences than at the inconvenience they may cause.

In addition to man's very limited control of natural forces and his own life span, he cannot control the time and circumstances of his birth or the historical, political, social, and economic events which preceded his birth—and, at best, he has only minimal influence over them during his own lifetime. The obsessive flatly refuses to accept this situation even though he is forced to live under these realistic limitations. He will deny the existence of such issues and will act as if he can live forever, or else maintain the myth that his death is solely the result of his own choice.

Dependency upon people is even more difficult for him than dependency upon objects. He deprecates peoples' usefulness or minimizes his need of them. When this is not possible he will try to rationalize his dependency by claiming that he is fulfilling the other person's needs and that actually it is the other person who is dependent upon him. At all times, however, he resents and criticizes the part of himself that requires help and is dependent upon others.

Marriage is difficult for the obsessional not only because of the degree of commitment which is required but also because of the inevitable dependencies that are a part of marriage. Unwittingly he comes to depend upon his partner and his family in a way that is highly satisfying, but also difficult to accept. Marriage serves to avoid loneliness and often produces satisfying emotional exchanges. It may be so rewarding that he cannot consider abandoning it and therefore feels trapped and resentful toward his partner. An awareness of this dependency may account for a great deal of the derogation and contempt which he expresses toward marriage and his mate. By such means he can minimize his feelings of dependency. He will criticize his wife at the same time as he will covertly lean on her for most of his needs. He may tyrannize his partner in order to maintain an illusion of power and independency. Thus he may appear to be "boss" or in control while it is actually he who is more dependent.

This dependency-independency struggle manifests itself in a tug of war for domination and control that is so regularly present in obsessional households. It is not long before the obsessional begins to feel that those he is dependent upon—whether it is his marital partner, his colleague, or a friend—are malevolent exploiters while he is a generous benefactor.

Every human activity requires some measure of commitment, and the degree of commitment is often determined by the individual's ability to be dependent. The word *commitment* implies a person's emotional and intellectual involvement in a project or relationship in which one's concern and interest is strong enough to make it a significant and meaningful activity. It is synonymous with the French word *engagement*. In recent years the philosophical explorations of the Existentialists have focused more attention on this aspect of human functioning. We can often permit ourselves to be totally committed in activities in which we have complete control, as we feel safe and secure from the powers of others to humiliate or hurt us. Fantasizing is such an activity and many people commit themselves to it with gusto and enthusiasm. On the other hand, since most activities are carried on with other people, we are subject to others' needs and desires as well as our own and cannot control the activity completely to suit our own interests. In such situations commitment may be tentative and cautious unless we can feel secure and trustful about the outcome.

It is a truism that one derives benefits from an experience in proportion to what one puts into it. Therefore the rewards that can be expected from an activity will depend upon the degree of commitment to it. Indifference, which is the antonym of commitment, reduces the possibilities of personal satisfaction in any activity. For some, frenzied activity and spurious enthusiasms cover up boredom, and cover up the difficulties of real commitment. Total commitment is difficult for anyone; it requires a feeling of total security.

In extreme states of insecurity and feelings of danger, which are characterized by flightiness and extreme distractibility, there is the absence of commitment. Such a state is often called *manic excitement*. When a person doubts his ability to control his living he also avoids commitments whenever possible. This is particularly true for the obsessional. He maximizes his control over his life by limiting his commitment, but at the same time he tends to minimize his satisfactions in living as well.

When the obsessional cannot avoid a commitment he will try to protect himself against the risks of involvement. This may involve prolonged investigation, and while it may serve a valid purpose by supplying necessary facts about a situation, it may discourage others from becoming involved with him. If he is forced to become involved, the commitment is often hedged with doubts, procrastinations, and "loopholes"—and even this degree of engagement may be postponed as long as possible.

An obsessional commitment is often made by default. For example, failure to act on a deadline produces effects which are equivalent to a commitment to some action or inaction. If one procrastinates about a down payment on a house, the house may be sold and the problem of whether to buy is settled by default.

This kind of a decision leaves the obsessional dissatisfied and not fully committed to the project. While he resents being pushed and forced by circumstances, he will often remove himself completely from making the decision by using cards, ouija boards, astrology, tea leaves, and other supernatural devices. A mistake or an unsatisfactory decision can then be blamed on fate, and he can feel justifiably aggrieved that fate never plays him a good turn. While such involvements may appear to be commitments, they lack the vital interest and dedication that come from making a personal choice. Under circumstances of default involvement is tentative, hesitant, and ambivalent. At times the obsessional may cast all caution aside and make an impulsive and rapid decision, claiming that time did not permit a careful examination of all the factors. This is another way of avoiding a full commitment.

Such was the case with a severely obsessive young man who studied the specifications of all the new model automobiles in order to make the best possible purchase. This was so involved and became so prolonged that by the time the survey was finished the new models arrived and he had to begin his survey all over again. This sequence continued for a few years until need finally forced him to make a choice. He then purchased the first car he saw on a used-car lot, a car which lacked all the engineering qualities he had until then considered absolutely essential. He took no responsibility for this choice, claiming that he was forced into the decision by the automobile industry.

Thus the obsessional rarely commits himself to a person or task even when his interest is very urgent. The dilemma of involvement without commitment is particularly emphasized in those professions wherein decisive actions cannot be avoided. The obsessional tends to become involved in sideline activities, such as sports, or in unrelated business ventures in which he allows himself total participation since his security does not depend exclusively upon the activity.

It is his fear of commitment which accounts for so much of the obsessional's indecisiveness. A young executive who was involved in a foreign financial activity was pushed into an obsessional panic when he was asked to choose between a post in western Europe or one in Asia. He was a bright and energetic person who was, however, quite obsessive. His decision had to serve too many contradictory requirements and he examined each alternative, balancing one against the other in an attempt to predict every possible consequence. When he leaned toward one choice the other immediately began to look better. He drew up charts, tables, and balance sheets, but when the deadline was reached he made his choice upon frivolous grounds. No sooner was it made than he began to regret not having made the other. As he felt that his choice had to be the perfect one, it was viewed as a life-and-death issue. One can understand the agony and anguish involved in making such a commitment.

TIME AND THE OBSESSIONAL

It is most significant that while the obsessional insists upon total freedom to remain uncommitted and to do whatever he pleases, his notions of freedom are absolute and extreme and he cannot acknowledge any form of restraint. Yet he demands such commitments from others. His apparent freedom and his choices are rigidly determined. The notion of being free as a justification for failing to become involved is spurious. His attitudes toward time illustrate his resistances to being committed to the present—thus the allure of the future.

Since time moves relentlessly onward, uninfluenced by man, it offers special burdens to the obsessional. He approaches it as an enemy to be fought and overcome, or dismissed as playing no role in his life. He will often behave as if he had an eternity in which to live and his projects and activities were not bounded by time at all. His plans therefore take no account of the realistic limitations of his life span, and his projects may encompass programs that require several lifetimes to fulfill.

It is preferable for him to maintain the illusion of absolute freedom and lack of involvement by excluding time as a realistic limitation on his life and regarding it as an enemy of all his plans and programs. Failure to take into account the element of time permits his plans to be so elaborate and time-consuming that he may never begin the projects. It is as if the obsessional would be admitting a weakness or a deficiency if he had to acknowledge his dependency upon time. Disregarding the realistic presence of time permits the obsessional to disregard normal sleep rhythms or schedules for eating, and to be irresponsible with regard to his appointments.

On the other hand, his devotion to decisiveness and precision forces him to be scrupulously prompt and to be intolerant of deviations by others. Such attitudes do not owe either to respect for time or to a recognition of its values; the obsessional is painfully aware of the future as an extension of the present since he is constantly preoccupied with guaranteeing the future. The "new" is significant only as it may play a role in guaranteeing the tomorrow. The present does not seem to exist for itself and is often without meaning or significance and must be tolerated or "killed" in order to arrive at the guaranteed and perfect future. Time in the present is often experienced as being wasted and as having no significance for itself; it must be passed through quickly in the obsessional's impatience to achieve the ideal tomorrow that never arrives.

Since he rarely considers the element of time as a factor in his activities, the obsessional organizes it poorly and has little ability to estimate its passage accurately. Long periods of time may be experienced as a few moments and invariably the estimate of "passed" time is incorrect. In order to overcome a persistent tendency to be late, one patient set his watch ahead. Instead of proceeding according to his watch, he would allow for extra time and then usually underestimate it and be later than he would have before he reset his watch. This tendency to underestimate the actual passage of time is almost always present in obsessionals.

Because his focus of interest is on the future, the obsessional's awareness of the present may be superficial and cursory; therefore his recall may be inadequate, sketchy, and at times, fallacious. Since the past is a collection of "presents" the obsessional's ability to recall his past is limited and uncertain.

Therefore, if the therapeutic process rests heavily on an accurate recall of the past, the obsessional presents many difficulties in this respect. Freud made this discovery very early in his research when he discovered that most of his obsessional patients described experiences of having been attacked sexually when in reality this had never occurred.

While the construction of the remote past may be distorted, the same problems pertain to the obsessional's recall of the recent past. His recollections are mainly in intellectual terms and he has great difficulty in identifying the emotional elements in these experiences. As the focus is on the future he cannot clearly understand that the past is a guide to the present, thus influencing his future. He appears to derive little benefit from past experiences and gets only temporary reassurance from the success of earlier performances. He has, therefore, little reverence for the past and its usefulness to his living.

Unless the present is an exact replica of the past, which it never can be, the obsessional feels a new challenge and a threat in each experience in spite of having resolved a similar situation in the past. There is little carry-over from his success in the past. This is evident in the phobic states, wherein prior confrontation and successful encounter with a phobic situation does not necessarily eliminate a repeated problem in the future. The past tends to become a clutter of irrelevant experiences except as it documents and fortifies the obsessional's neurotic needs and programs.

Because of the obsessional's disregard for time he soon discovers that he does not have enough time to complete even the most modest project. His commitments to a task are seriously disrupted because he has no real involvements with the element of time. In order to assemble a hi-fi player, for example, he may insist on first becoming an expert in electronic speakers and amplifiers. This turns into an impossible task for which enough time is never available. Before the day is over many tasks are still incomplete and he is dissatisfied because time has run out and he must go to bed. Sleep is invariably postponed because he refuses to abandon his activities. There is never enough time to work or enough time to rest.

Insomnia is related to the problem of "giving up" and abandoning controls; it is quite prevalent in obsessional individuals. Under these circumstances, the insomniac becomes tense and uneasy when he feels he is falling asleep. He attempts to regain control, but to get to sleep he must slowly relinquish it; as soon as he does he becomes more alert in order to regain it. This goes on until fatigue overcomes him and he can no longer stay awake.

Comparisons

The obsessional's view of time is unlike that of the hysteric, who is more actively concerned with time in the here and now. For the hysteric the present performance—with its possibilities for influencing the immediate environment—occupies his focus of interest. Tomorrow is an abstraction that is of no concern to him now; he is interested in the effect which his performance is achieving at this moment. Prospective considerations, planning, foresight, and utilization of past experiences for the present to determine the future are alien to the hysterical individual and the hysterical performance.

For the depressed person, on the other hand, time exists only as it transpired in the past. The present has no value and the future is without possibility. Time has stopped. It has no significance for him except as it was, and the passage of time is a burden that he cannot surmount.

The preoccupation with the past, in the depressions, leads to a stagnation and an absence of planning for the future. For the obsessional, planning and programming for the future occupies the bulk of his time. The hysteric neither looks to the past nor plans for the future; he counts only the next moment of his existence.

This latter style of living characterizes other immature types of personality, notably the psychopath, who emphasizes the distrust of past and future in favor of what is now available. His philosophy is "a dollar now is better than two in the future." This type of orientation is related to a great distrust of the future; the person hasn't the confidence in his own ability to anticipate a favorable future, or else is convinced of a malevolence which will deny him any future possibilities. Therefore, he must grab all he can right now—not to do so is inconceivable. There is only a limited capacity to postpone gratification of all kinds, since there is a strong suspicion that such gratification will not be available later. Only the present moment has any reality for such a person. This is strikingly true for some obese people who must eat all they can at each meal as if no food will be available at the next meal. They are unable to postpone any gratification as they have no confidence that the future will be able to provide for them. They have no conviction that what they do not eat now will be available later.

Erwin Strauss, an Existential psychiatrist, has viewed the obsessional process as a failure to deal with time as a realistic accompaniment of living. The obsessional person is preoccupied with decay and disintegration. Everything is viewed as relation to the future, since the past has no reality and the present is dead or already decaying. The obsessional has a great need to deny death and acts as if it will never occur. While he abhors death, he finds the notion of a timeless eternity equally frightening. Death, decay, destruction, violence, anything dealing with uncontrollable elements of human existence must be kept out of awareness. Strauss believes that the obsessional develops many rituals in order to maintain the dissociation of these unacceptable ideas. Since the obsessional is not able to deny entirely the evidences of death and decay around him, he often has a compulsive fascination with them.

The compulsive need to deny death as a reality often leads to a reckless disregard of danger; the person may push himself beyond the boundaries of normal exertion. He may expose himself to dangers that others would ordinarily protect themselves from. Unlike the mature person, he cannot utilize an understanding of the past as a guide to more adequate performance in the present as a solid basis for his future existence.

MARRIAGE AND THE OBSESSIONAL

The marriage commitment is particularly difficult for the obsessional because it involves interpersonal issues as well as legal sanction. Since it is possible to achieve some degree of control over things through intelligence or know-how, the obsessional can manage some power in his dealings with objects or ideas. Emotions and feelings enter into the relationships with one's fellow-man and these elements are much harder to control—so that the degree of control over interpersonal relationships is always far less than is possible in nonpersonal relationships. The commitments are always partial, contingent, and if possible, have an escape route. When no legal or social ties bind the relationship there is always a threat of dissolution from one moment to the next.

While marriage has legal binds, the marriage commitment may still be minimal. As time goes on, however, the obsessional comes to enjoy the commitment if the atmosphere offers some security. It may even encourage greater closeness. The early days of an obsessional marriage can be extremely difficult, but if the marriage survives, it may prove to be quite therapeutic. However, the demands for perfection and the critical and derogating behavior that the obsessional brings to a marriage may prove to be too much to withstand. This is especially so when there is only a minimum of warmth and affection present. The obsessional's insistence on "honesty" leads him to tell all, regardless of its effect upon his partner; unless some enduring qualities are present to override such arrogance, disaster may very likely occur. However, as the obsessional has difficulty in admitting a mistake or acknowledging a failure, he may postpone dissolving the marriage so that in the long run it may work out after all.

When both partners are obsessional, the complications are increased geometrically. This is not an uncommon situation; in spite of the well-known aphorism that opposites attract, only an obsessional can feel comfortable with another obsessional. The courtship is characterized by cautious restraint (which pleases both partners) and the decision to marry is followed by many postponements and delays accompanied by uncertainties and uneasiness on both sides. As long as the demands upon each other are minimal and neither partner feels trapped, all goes well and the marriage may work out. These marriages are punctuated by frequent and dramatic power struggles in which each obsessional partner is striving to gain the advantage. A draw is the most frequent outcome. The relationship is characterized by minimal commitment on each side, while each partner demands maximal commitment from the other. Often when the relationship is moving along nicely, one partner may pull away to avoid the possibility of too intense an involvement. As one pulls away, however, the other pushes harder in order to be reassured. Such pressures are interpreted as power ploys and produce further withdrawal in the partner. The situation produces the typical neurotic spiral wherein the fear of rejection requires gestures of reassurance but instead produces further rejection. At one point the rejected individual gives up and may make no further demands. At that time the partner stops withdrawing and may proceed to demand assurances, since he is not being pursued. This temporarily breaks the vicious circle and if the marriage provides some benefits, these limited demonstrations of need and affection may be the only tender moments the couple has.

Such see-saw movements are quite common and the symbiotic balance is maintained because there is some commitment, even though it is minimal. There is a covert agreement of limited involvement in the marriage and each partner pursues his own interests and desires though they each share in the common responsibilities. While pursuing their individual needs they occasionally call upon each other to fill those satisfactions that require a partner. Mingling and companionship are part of this agreement and each partner knows the limits and extents of these boundaries. Failure to respect these rights and limits is a frequent cause of marital difficulties in such situations. Intimacy is achieved to a limited degree, and as the years roll by, the boundaries of the commitment to one another may even be extended.

Marriages such as these are generally loaded with elaborate bookkeeping systems to make certain that one partner does not give or get more than the other. Accounting of contributions—whether of time or money or who did the dishes last—is generally accurately recorded in the account book or the memory of each partner. Concessions, compromises, sacrifices, and contributions need to be equalized so that neither partner is taken advantage of. Love, affection, gifts, etc., are also handled in this way; to give too much affection might be read as too great an involvement. Besides, one partner might presume that such displays are evidence of unconditional commitment, so that he will take advantage of the other. If one gives too much, the partner may interpret this as coming from a great need, which would indicate a weakness. One needs to keep his partner in doubt as to how he stands in the relationship in order to exercise some degree of control over it. This is how the obsessional limits the danger when closeness cannot be avoided. To play it safe he must be able to detach himself quickly from the relationship, should it become necessary.

These marriages are often conditional in every sense and the marriage was probably made possible in the first place because the partners agreed in advance that if all did not go well they could get a quick and easy divorce. This type of agreement limits the commitment at the outset and while it may be necessary in order that the marriage take place, it provides the basis for the later dissolution.

Such relationships are continually under tension and seem to consist of a multitude of games in a tug-of-war to establish a degree of safety and security by having some measure of control over the other person. Love is the main piece of equipment and it is used in a variety of ways to gain and hold the advantage. The goal is to guarantee one's own security and to fulfill one's own needs without offending or alienating the other person by withholding too much. A proper balance must be struck and this requires great skill in the art of gamemanship. By giving enough to stir up expectations and promised return, but not too much so as to imply that one is "gone" and available, the obsessional hopes to maintain a fine balance that will ensure a stable relationship while retaining sufficient autonomy to dissolve it without too great stress or pain.

The obsessional hopes and expects that he will advance his strivings for perfection and absolute control in his marriage. His wife will overcome his deficiencies. She should be free, spontaneous, warm and tender, decisive and secure. She should have social graces and the ability to charm all the people that he would tend to alienate. If, however, she does have these qualities, he tends to criticize and derogate her and her petty concerns. On her side, his high standards and perfectionistic demands as well as his grandiose conceptions of himself have undoubtedly led her to the hope of some fulfillment through his presumed strength and power, which, she assumes, will lead him to the pinnacle of success. Such hopes and unrealistic expectations are doomed to disappointment and create much dissension in the marriage because each partner is able honestly to claim that he or she made no promises, and that the expectations came from the other's own neurotic demands.

When very rigid and uncompromising obsessionals marry there are few possibilities for success. Every marriage, regardless of how overt the understanding of limited commitment, requires some "give and take" and the necessity of abandoning total control of the partner. Unless one is prepared for some compromise, the partner will reach a point beyond which he will refuse to go. At this point the marriage will dissolve, since the demand to be right will overcome even the minimal rewards of marriage. It then becomes a game of "chicken," and fatal results ensue when neither partner will give way. Disaster can be averted only when one partner is prepared to acknowledge that a stubborn refusal to compromise endangers both partners. When obsessionals marry the difficulty ultimately gets back to the limitations of commitment which minimize the responsibility for the success of the marriage.

SEX BEHAVIOR AND THE OBSESSIONAL

While the particular patterns of sex behavior may vary in each obsessional, depending upon his idiosyncratic experiences and background, they are also influenced to a greater or lesser extent by the typical characterologic attitudes involved in the obsessional defense. The need for perfection and the resistance to any involvement or commitment, coupled with an uneasiness about receiving or giving tenderness, greatly influences his sexual behavior. The issue of control and the fear of loss of control, which are essential elements in the sex act and in the obsessional system, are responsible for many complications in his sex life.

Although Freud assumed that a normal sex life was incompatible with neurosis, it is surprising how often the obsessional person, with either mild or severe symptoms, manages a satisfactory sexual adjustment. He can often perform the sex act properly and so that it will conform with the latest sex manuals and acceptable sex practices. Due consideration is given to the partner—according to the latest psychiatric theories. The act itself, however, is stilted, unspontaneous and routinized. Experimentation is avoided or carried out according to a program. While this approach may be entirely satisfactory for the male partner it may be unsatisfactory for the woman. At other times, it may be mutually enjoyable, as in the quest for a perfect performance much care is given to the needs of the female.

The sexual enlightenment which followed Freud's discoveries encouraged the female to expect and demand some satisfaction from the sex act, while promoting a series of notions that could produce further difficulties. For the female, orgasm became a realizable goal and as a result of her newly acquired knowledge it was assigned as a responsibility of the male. This, however, was only the first step towards a perfect sex act. Mutual and simultaneous orgasm was also expected. Since it is already difficult for the obsessional female to achieve an orgasm, the expectation of simultaneous orgasm as a usual outcome is generally impossible to fulfill.

In addition to these complications, the assumption of two types of orgasm in the female (vaginal and clitoral) and the notion that one was more mature and therefore more desirable, was also popularized by psychoanalytic theory. This assumption was not based on psychological evidence, but was the result of applying the libido theory to the female. It was a necessary postulate to make the elaborate psychosexual development scheme for the male fit the pattern of sexual development for the female. Finally, the tendency to view the male as the active sex partner and the female as the passive sex partner has encouraged doubts about one's sexual potency and adequacy when one's desires and interests run counter to this assumption.

While the notion of orgasm for the female is a justifiable expectation, the insistence on the simultaneous orgasm is an idealized notion encouraged by the overzealous and mistaken view of the possibilities of psychoanalytic therapy. This has placed a burden on both partners; they should achieve this desirable goal or else feel that each has failed and that the relationship must be a bad one. However, under even the best of circumstances, simultaneous orgasm is not common. In spite of the obsessional's capacity to control his ejaculation in order to achieve the ideal orgasm for his wife, such perfect timing is often impossible and cannot be expected to occur every time.

The assumption of dual orgasms, however, has produced even more mischief and distress—not only in obsessional marriages but in every other kind. This notion is popularly interpreted as an orgasm which is achieved only by the use of the penis in the vagina. If any other stimulation is used, such as a finger or other kind of friction on the clitoris, it is considered to be a clitoral orgasm and therefore both imperfect and immature. The obsessional female already has enough difficulties in "letting go," and requires a great deal more clitoral stimulation than is usually necessary. The failure to achieve orgasm with or without manual manipulation may not only make the woman feel inadequate, but may also leave a feeling of failure in the male who has been unsuccessful in producing an orgasm for her.

Consequently, this concept, which has questionable validity, has complicated and aggravated the obsessional's sex life. Instead of being an occasion of intimacy and potential pleasure it becomes a test and trial of his adequacy. Efforts involving the use of the hands or the mouth to improve the possibility of pleasure are considered evidence of immaturity or perversity. The concern about producing an orgasm for the woman often results in premature ejaculation as a result of the tension involved in the efforts to prolong the sex act. Premature ejaculation is the result of anxiety which produces a loss of control in the male. In contrast to the female, where anxiety and tension interfere with the relaxation required for an orgasm, the male responds by ejaculating too quickly. The presence of anxiety severely handicaps the sexual activities of obsessional couples.

The Element of Control

The need to be in control at all times, even during the sex act, prevents the woman from allowing something to happen to her. Instead, she must manage her own orgasm and do it herself. The sex act ordinarily proceeds with a gradual increase in tension of the entire musculature, particularly in the pelvic area. The orgasm is a climax of a release of tension and relaxation of the musculature. Ejaculation in the male is the result of a spasmodic contraction of the urethral musculature followed by muscular relaxation. Therefore at some point the female must "let go'" or abandon control, just as the male ultimately abandons control to allow ejaculation to occur. It is an instance of human functioning; in order to allow some activity to proceed one must give up trying to force it to happen. The physiology of sphincter action most clearly demonstrates this paradox: the tension produced by active efforts to force open a sphincter tends to close it even more tightly. To allow the sphincter to open one must relax and give up the "forcing." Thus, anxiety about one's physiological functions may increase the tension and prevent the relaxation required to allow orgasm to occur. In trying desperately to achieve orgasm during intercourse, the obsessional female will generally manage it only after her husband has ejaculated; then, with manual massage of her clitoris, accompanied by extensive fantasizing in which the entire sexual performance is under her control, orgasm can be achieved.

Interestingly, when the issue of control is not crucial, such as in fleeting relationships or if intimacy is entirely lacking, the sex act may be far more successful. This explains the contradictory situation in which the sex act can be far more satisfactory with paramours, prostitutes, or single encounters than with one's own wife. The use of alcohol or other relaxants will also enhance the possibilities of enjoyment for the woman as well as the man.

In general, however, the need to control influences the male's performance far less than the female's. Control over his ejaculation may improve the possibility of orgasm in the female, providing he does not get too anxious about it and thereby bring on premature ejaculation.

The assignment of specific and limited behavioral qualities to each sex—such as activity as a male requisite and passivity as a female attribute—has played special havoc with the sex life of the obsessional. This notion has been widely accepted, and only in recent years has it been shown that the female, instead of being a passive recipient, plays an active participating role in the sex act. She is more than a mere receptacle and her sexual organs, particularly the vaginal canal, play an active role in drawing and transporting the sperm up into the uterus. However, the prevailing conception of sexual roles—which requires that the male be the aggressive initiator of the sex act while the female wait patiently to be invited—has greatly aggravated role problems for obsessional couples because control is considered to be entirely the prerogative of the male and activity or initiative on the part of the female is marked as unfeminine and immature. The lusty and sexy female has needed to inhibit her passion or suffer critical condemnation while the withdrawn, inactive female has been supported by the cultural prejudices toward passivity; any inclinations toward active involvement during or before the sex act had to be restrained. Similarly, the male who might need some reassurance from a supportive or expressive wife was forced to be the initiator and active participant. Any interest in allowing his wife to be more active might be judged as unmasculine. This pattern could also be related directly to the notion of "who is on top" in the sex act. This is a significant matter for the obsessional; therefore a positional variation could be the basis for considerable distress in this type of person. However, reversing positions in the sex act can frequently provide greater satisfaction for the female by allowing her greater freedom of motion and better control of her movements during coitus. Physiologically it enhances the possibility of achieving orgasm. For the male, it can also be a most enjoyable variation—provided he does not view it as "feminine." However, popular prejudice—initiated and encouraged by scientific misconception—has interfered with this variation of sex activity and has produced fear and guilt with the implication that the position is indicative of homosexual tendencies. Such labels discourage experimentation and exploration. For the obsessional who is already burdened with problems, such prohibitions increase his difficulties. The female is prevented from enhancing her possibilities for achieving orgasm while the male is prevented from the beneficial abandonment of some control in the sex act.

Mutuality and "Guarantees"

Sex should be mutual activity in which each participant feels free to be both active and passive, giving and receiving—without concern as to who is doing the giving or receiving at each moment. Since the goal is pleasure, "who is on top" is significant only in terms of whether it is pleasureable for that couple. The obsessional's reticence about sex is the outcome of his problems in other areas of living. Since he is already insecure and restrained, the conventional notions of masculinity and feminity throw additional burdens on his sex activities.

Added to the burden of producing or achieving orgasm is the obsessional's need for guaranteed performances, which require rigid sexual patterns in which curiosity and experimentation are dangerous. Unless he can have some assurances, either personal or cultural, that his excursions will not produce additional dangers he will not attempt them. He must secure, if possible, control over his performance. This requirement often leads him to make appointments for his sex activity, thus preventing spontaneous demands or refusals; such arrangements may be made days or hours in advance. They need not be verbal, and generally such arrangements are made by signals tacitly acknowledged by both partners. This eliminates the possibility of a direct refusal or rejection, as the signals need not be acknowledged. While such arrangements minimize the risks of being rejected, they also reduce the spontaneous quality of sex, which can be a source of great pleasure. Instead, the act becomes more like a business deal—routinized and properly executed—rather than a response to passion or love. The sexual patterns of obsessionals are inevitably influenced by the partial involvement and commitment of the partners.

The impasse about sex is overcome when the sex needs of one partner become so strong that he will yield and make a gesture of surrender which will allow intercourse to take place. After a passage of time, however, grievances begin to accumulate again and the need to exert control takes the upper hand. This forces the partner to become defensive and the vicious circle is set up again.

This drama was reenacted regularly in the life of a young obsessional couple who played out their roles with almost total lack of awareness. Sex was a game in which each partner awaited a signal from the other before proceeding. After a respectable waiting period following the previous sexual episode, the man would look increasingly hurt and neglected, hoping to force his wife to make a positive gesture which would then allow him to take a more definitive step to initiate sex activity again. The wife, in turn, would delay the gesture as long as possible, waiting until her husband's pained demeanor would make her feel guilty. She would then give the signal, by way of taking a shower, or by going to bed early. Her husband was almost totally preoccupied with sex and whether he could succeed in getting his wife to agree. While his pride and manliness were at stake, his notion that he was thoughtful and considerate of his wife was his justification for not taking the initiative by direct action. She, in turn, would try to postpone agreement as long as possible. Her role was always that of the martyr who agreed in order to please him, although her real aim was that of appeasing her guilt. Sex was never discussed between them and therefore neither partner knew for sure what the game or the rules were. The situation would proceed as follows: upon arrival from work, the husband would scrutinize his wife for gestures of friendliness that he could interpret as a sexual invitation. In order to avoid his tendencies to misinterpret her gestures, she would have to be careful not to be too warm or accepting. Instead she might announce a new symptom of some physical discomfort, or regale him with stories about how tired she was or how much work she needed to do. This was invariably interpreted (and not always correctly) as a notice of evasion. At first he would find this mildly irritating, but after a few days it would visibly annoy him. If she would question him at these times, he would deny being angry. As he got more annoyed, however, he would avoid all friendly gestures. This would be the signal to her that sex was necessary to forestall further difficulty with him and she would proceed to give him some sign announcing her intention and permitting him to be sure about the acceptance of his advances. As there were long delays and a continuing "trial" of his potency, the sex act invariably terminated in premature ejaculation, followed by a long session of manual manipulation to enable her to achieve an orgasm. Intercourse occurred only when the two were annoyed, guilty, angry at each other, or sexually starved. It was small wonder that the sex act was not pleasurable for them.

On other occasions when the tug of war would become tiresome and both partners were more friendly, sex activity would be agreed upon long in advance and preparations would be made which exaggerated the significance of the occasion. It was never the outgrowth of a spontaneous warmth, friendliness or lustful desire. Instead of an occasion for romantic fun, it became a great event designed to deal with many issues.

This tug of war was directly related to the inability of either partner to relinquish control of the marriage in general and sex in particular. There was too much at stake in maintaining the position of a strong, controlled, and uncomplaining partner whose love was so great as to outweigh the inadequacy of the sex performance. Each had to be firm and resolute and not expose his need for the other to see for fear of being hurt, rejected, and despised as a weakling. The inability to let go and deal with sex as an experience rather than a therapeutic event was manifest in the woman's incapacity to have orgasm except after prolonged manipulation which produced so much weariness that she could no longer exert any control. She resented not being able to have an orgasm by herself and of having to be dependent upon her husband. Most often her orgasm would be achieved when clitoral manipulation was accompanied by fantasies of being overwhelmed and having control taken away from her. Again, the issue of control, so central to the obsessional disorder, interfered strikingly with the sex life of this couple.

One of the remarkable benefits from psychotherapeutic work with both husband and wife was the marked improvement in their sex life. The release of the need to control and recognition of the mutually destructive patterns enabled them to enjoy sex and make it an experience of pleasure and mutual exchange and commitment. The husband could prolong the act before ejaculating and his wife's orgasms became more frequent. Sex was not avoided, and for the first time in their marriage, they began to look forward to intercourse as a more spontaneous experience.

As has been suggested earlier, the obsessional has no conviction of the possibility of obtaining tenderness gratuitously; he feels it must be earned through good works. While the development of tender, loving relationships requires both activity and concern, it cannot be achieved exclusively through deliberate promotion and calculated effort. Warmth and intimacy grow out of tender exchanges implicit in meaningful relationships. One can not buy, nor can one *demand*, tenderness from another through exploitation or by barter. It often comes unasked, and can be achieved simply when one is available and friendly. The obsessional can neither comprehend nor believe this in spite of much evidence to the contrary in his marriage. The uncertainty and distrust of his likeableness makes him suspicious of any tenderness that comes spontaneously to him; if it is unearned, he cannot accept it comfortably. When it occurs in this way he responds with contempt for the giver, whom he feels must be weak and a "sucker." He may also become suspicious of the giver's motives, feeling that the tenderness is a device to manipulate and control him. This makes marital exchanges extremely difficult.

Since the other person's tender activities are viewed with caution and suspicion, every move must be countered by a gambit in which one tries to get the advantage and the control over the relationship. The experience of tenderness is viewed as a move in an ongoing struggle. In the struggle, strong negative feelings are generally not openly expressed. Such feelings, however, can accumulate and become so overwhelming that the obsessional feels guilty and expects retribution. The guilt feelings may produce exaggerated displays of affection and interest which may take on a begging and obsequious tone. This type of behavior may make him angry at himself as well as with his partner, because he views it as weak and as evidence of being under the control of the other person. It kindles his destructive fantasies and sets the vicious circle into motion again.

The obsessional person may rationalize this reaction by implying that the hostility and destructiveness come from the other person and that his reaction is a response to it. He justifies his behavior by implying that the other person, if permitted, would overwhelm and disintegrate him and therefore it is necessary for him to actively oppose and overcome the opponent. In sex or outside it, the obsessional's capacity for tender exchanges is seriously hampered; he operates in the borderlands of uncertainty as to how he stands with regard to other people—even in a marriage that seems to be proceeding well or in sex activity that is pleasureable.

CHAPTER 4

The Obsessive Spectrum

Every human is limited in his capacity to influence each aspect of his existence. Sometimes he may be irritated when physical incapabilities or limitations prevent him from doing all that he might wish to do. It is only when the person attempts to achieve superhuman goals that his human frailties become truly noticeable. A wide variety of devices are employed to evade or deny such limitations. Belief in eternal life or reincarnation and the delusion of omnipotent control are attempts to evade this kind of awareness. Jules Masserman has called these the unconscious or *Ur* delusions of mankind.

Such tendencies are omnipresent. Many of the measures employed can be recognized as aspects of the obsessional syndrome. The degree of uneasiness and uncertainty that one experiences will range from feeling endangered at all times to a state of relative ease and security in which only the gross, existential dangers —such as the awareness of one's ultimate death—need to be dealt with. While the use of obsessional patterns is found in all human behavior, it will vary according to one's need for guarantees and certainties. There is, therefore, a broad spectrum of obsessional behavior ranging from the normal (i.e., the amount that enables one to function without undue anxiety) to that which pervades a person's living whether it impedes that living or impairs his performance or not. If it is present in greater amounts and manifests itself in distressing or incapacitating symptoms, it is called "neurotic." This means that the obsessional patterns are sufficiently encompassing and determinative that they interfere with constructive and productive living.

Why are some individuals less secure than others in an emotional sense? What factors determine the sense of danger and threat that permeates the life of such people? These are the focal questions in all psychiatric formulations because the defense mechanisms which are utilized in one's living are attempts to deal with feelings of insecurity and threats to emotional integrity. Does the obsessional defense have some specificity? For instance, why do some people utilize the hysterical mode of dealing with anxiety while others tend to become obsessional? This is a difficult and elusive problem, involving the matter of choice of symptoms in neurotic and psychotic disorders. Clearly, constitutional factors play a role in this choice, as do the parental patterns which become the emotional environment of the growing individual. The nature of the real threats is also involved—whether they are economic, political, or historical. It is a complex issue in which monocausal explanations have no place. Yet there are some factors that can be related more clearly to one type of defense than to another.

If the obsessional pattern is heavily involved with control it would tend to be present in situations in which the infant or child found himself unable to handle the demands that were made upon him. For example, a child whose early experiences of being able to please or manipulate the adults through his repertoire of assorted behavioral devices might develop feelings of personal power—the capacity to control and influence the world around him. Such would be in contrast to the child who is unable to please, manipulate, or influence significant adults regardless of what he does or how hard he tries. The second child is left with feelings of doubt and uncertainty about his capacities and may develop an obsessional personality or an obsessive neurosis at some time in his life. The first child will tend to have fewer obsessional patterns in his living.

The need to defy, control, or comply as an expression of self-esteem and self-worth comes to play a vital role in the developmental situation, depending upon the amount of freedom, coercion, or manipulation coming from the significant adults. If the pressures are extreme, the individual may need to defy or rebel in order to express his own self-esteem. The defiance may become automatic or compulsive and be detrimental to the growing personality. It can produce a rigid, negativistic person instead of one with a strong sense of will. Some of these issues are part of many theories which center around the process of bowel training or discipline in general as related to the origin of the obsessional disorders. The role of early patterning of obsessional behavior is undoubted, as is the influence of the parental figures and their own obsessional difficulties. It is conceivable that there could not be a severe obsessional problem in the child unless it were already present in the parents.

DEVELOPMENTAL FACTORS

Many observers have noted that particular developmental stages in human growth tend to be more closely related to obsessional development than others. Freud stressed bowel training. Certainly the matter of control is an essential ingredient in bowel training, as it is in all sphincter activity. The periods during which the outside world may make excessive or extreme demands in terms of fulfilling the cultural modes may stimulate obsessional patterns, tending to promote or accelerate any already-existing doubts and apprehensions about oneself. Similarly, stages of juvenile conformity or the patterning of social or sexual behavior to conform with adult demands may be the impetus for obsessional developments. Therefore, phobias and other obsessional manifestations may be more prominent at certain periods of development than at others.

A brief excerpt from the early experiences of a severe obsessional illustrates the relationship of parental demands upon a child whose physical defect required cautious concern from the parents: At the age of four the patient lost an eye in an unfortunate accident. In her anxiety to protect his good eye, his mother was excessively vigilant about all his physical activities. She felt comfortable about him only when he was at home studying. Consequently, academic achievement was stressed far beyond everything else. Nothing less than the best in his class was acceptable. The constant preoccupation with caution and safety in what was pictured for him as a potentially dangerous world made him unable to deal with the universe without a host of phobias and rituals. These began at an early age and continued throughout his life. When he reached 18, he had a widespread obsessional neurosis which impaired his effectiveness, in spite of exceptional mathematical skills. His tardy, irresponsible and indecisive tendencies produced occupational complications which required psychoanalytic treatment.

He had an overpowering need to be in absolute control of himself and the universe at every moment in order to guarantee his safety and maintain his delusion of omnipotent control. He had grown up in an atmosphere charged with danger at every moment, and it was this feeling of ever-present threat which determined his neurotic need to establish guarantees and certainties in his living, rather than any particular trauma or specific series of events.

Although the beginnings of the obsessional defense mechanisms can often be fixed around that stage associated with the development of sphincter control, or traced to a response to ambivalent attitudes toward one's parents, it is also associated with a general atmosphere of doubt and uncertainty about one's ability to modify or influence the environment to satisfy one's needs. The history of obsessional development is as varied as one's environment and the personality of one's parents. The consistent theme in all obsessionals is the presence of anxieties about being in danger because of an incapacity to fulfill the requirements of others and to feel certain of one's acceptance. Sexual complications in the early years—which were also presumed to play a role in the etiology of the obsessional state—can rarely be identified. However, the obsessional frequently does experience sexual problems and he views them as evidence of his incapacity to function in an effective manner.

It is evident that all reasonably effective human beings want to live in an atmosphere in which their skills and intelligence can afford them some guarantee of the outcome of their activity. All humans are motivated to some extent by the expectation of success in achieving their goals. They exercise foresight by using the hindsight of experience and the benefits derived from it. Their plans are based on minimizing risks by foreseeing possible complications and difficulties. However, most people are also aware that not all possible dangers or potential risks and complications can be anticipated and overcome. Unforeseen changes, unexpected complications, accidental, coincidental, and cataclysmic events can always occur which may often demand an alteration in one's plans. In general, such complications are met and dealt with, and plans are not simply abandoned because everything cannot be accurately anticipated. Because of these ever-present potential complications and the human incapacity to fully control and influence them, man has always needed some devices—rational or irrational—to minimize the difficulties. As he could not affect them directly, he utilized magical devices, delusions of omnipotent controls, rituals, and the whole gamut of techniques described in earlier chapters to give him the illusion of greater control than he possessed.

If this picture of the role of obsessional techniques is valid, then it would also follow that as man's security increased his use of obsessional devices would diminish. One would expect a decrease of obsessional practices as man's grasp of the universe extended. Instead, there are evidences of the widespread use of obsessional techniques in all cultures. Certainly the manifestations are more manifest when they are culturally encouraged and are less in evidence when they are derided by the culture. At all times, however, the amount of obsessional practice in each individual varies widely according to his own personal and idiosyncratic experiences. A wide spectrum of obsessional behavior will be found, depending upon the individual's personal security and based on his intellectual and emotional development and the awareness of his powers and its limitations.

At one extreme is a minimum of obsessional patterns, ones that are barely noticeable under ordinary circumstances. At the other extreme, the patterns are so pervasive as to interfere with productive living. In the first extreme, which we may call "normal," obsessional defenses may even enhance one's performance. In the opposite extreme they may produce neurotic or psychotic behavior and may seriously impair one's capacity for living. Between these two extremes are the "more or less" obsessional defenses which are sometimes identified as a cluster of personality patterns called *obsessional personality*. The total population may be roughly classified into three groups: (1) normal utilization of obsessional defenses; (2) obsessional personality structure; and (3) obsessional neurosis.

In spite of the widespread presence of the obsessional behavioral pattern there is a tendency in some cultures to use the term "obsessional" as a pejorative label. Even when the value of such behavior is held in high esteem—such as in neatness or order —it becomes derogatory if it is labelled *obsessional*. The term may also be used to belittle someone else's performance when one feels either envious or competitive toward him. In this way the term is often used as a critical one and the behavior associated with it is derided or condemned. Often the psychiatrist, psychologist, or social worker, in misplaced zeal, identifies and labels symptoms with the notion that identification is itself therapeutic. There is a tendency to view the ability to supply labels as evidence of one's skill as a therapist.

This type of labelling, however, can be both destructive and unprofitable for the patient; it may produce anxiety which will require further obsessional defenses. In addition, when the defensive obsessional patterns which have been valuable to the individual's integration are merely spotlighted and labelled, they may no longer be effective and the hitherto stable equilibrium may be prematurely and unwisely disrupted. The utilization of obsessional defenses varies not only from person to person, but may even vary in the same person at different times. As the situation changes and the pressure increases, obsessional patterns in the same individual may become more and more extensive and while they were originally within manageable limits, may become sufficiently widespread to blossom into an obsessional neurosis. Once the patterns become this severe, they generally tend to become more and more extensive and more and more incapacitating. This is the typical vicious circle of the neuroses, in which some of the attempts to relieve the distress of the neurotic involvements only produce further anxiety and more nerotic reactions to the anxiety. While this is true of any nerotic development, it is particularly true in the obsessional neurosis.

If additional burdens and stresses are placed on the obsessional neurotic there can be a further disintegration of functioning—with the resulting development of a schizophrenic reaction. While this particular development is fortunately not common, it does form the basis for a plausible theory regarding the origin of schizophrenia.

NORMAL OBSESSIONAL BEHAVIOR

While the above designation may appear to be contradictory, it is preferred only because the word "obsessional" is usually used as if it always implies pathologic changes whereas it may well include the multitude of .obsessional patterns which serve constructive and adaptive purposes in human functioning. The difficulty arises when we try to define the criteria for identifying obsessional behavior which can be considered well within the range of normal behavior. Can we be certain that it is useful or productive, in contrast to the neurotic's obsessional patterns? How do we know when the normal obsessional patterns become sufficiently extensive so that we can now call it an obsessional personality structure?

While the differentiation is not particularly significant for theoretical reasons, it has much value in enabling the therapist to clarify his own thinking about which patterns should become the target for study and possible elimination and which should be left undisturbed. This is not a decision to be made by the therapist alone, but one for the patient as well, and is intimately related to the value of the pattern in the individual's total living. However, such a determination is often beyond the scope of the individual as at the outset the obsessional does not want to eliminate his obsessional patterns—rather he wishes to improve and perfect them so that they will be invulnerable. It is the responsibility of the therapist to highlight the destructive aspects of the such patterns of behavior and to reduce their role in the patient's life.

It is clear that obsessional behavior can increase one's efficiency and effectiveness in performing certain tasks. The tenacity which characterizes the obsessional often enables him to pursue his tasks with single-minded dedication. An awareness of the limit of this dedication may help to decide which patterns require psychiatric scrutiny and which, even if peculiar, should not be tampered with.

For example, in the anxiety not to throw anything away lest it yield information, the obsessional may actually accumulate collections of historical, esthetic, or commercial value. Many of these collections are rationalized on the basis that the items may be needed at some future time, and since one never knows when that might be, it is safer to save everything and throw nothing away. This may result in collections of buttons, strings, bric-a-brac, etc. Occasionally, it will include a hard-to-get item. Usually it would be more useful and perhaps even more economical to get rid of the old and buy anew when the need arises. However, the obsessional cannot chance this. His collections are attempts to guarantee that his needs will always be fulfilled. To throw something away is an irreversible act and one that carries a certain amount of risk.

Occasionally this tendency to accumulate can be productive and become the basis for a career or a trade. Unless it is unmanageable and begins to interfere with one's living, it should not be labelled neurotic or even noted with the pejorative term "obsessional." It might be viewed as odd, and if it is excessive enough to be noticed, it might evince some concern in the person himself. Ordinarily, however, the collecting tendency is a part of the person's life which produces some clutter and some periodic annoyance, but does not become severe enough to be unmanageable. The person still has some choice; he may often recognize the excesses and may even begin to limit this tendency in many areas. Such people are still dealing with obsessional patterns which are within normal range.

The matter can also be considered from the point of view of the purpose of the collecting—particularly as to what underlies or motivates the collector. Clarification is important to determine whether some therapeutic intervention may be necessary. The criteria of adaptation, which can be applied, are very useful in recognizing whether the tendency is incapacitating or not. On the other hand, the person who collects on the assumption that the articles may have some value in the future differs from the person who collects because he cannot give anything up. The latter acts as if the supplies of everything in the universe are limited, and to abandon anything means to lose it forever. This type of person is a hoarder, and he may collect anything and everything. His anxiety arises from a different order of concern than that of the obsessional. The hoarder's collections are often purposeless and meaningless in contrast to those of the obsessional.

The latter may discard the objects as soon as they have served their purpose; the hoarder can never give up anything. His total preoccupation is collecting; the obsessional collects to achieve perfection and omniscience.

Obsessional collecting, however, is not far removed from hoarding and can easily become a total preoccupation. The distinction is qualitative as well as quantitative, and the same gradation can be seen in other obsessional patterns as well. For example, the concern for preciseness and accuracy can be a great asset in those professions or crafts in which faultless behavior is both necessary and possible. It is highly valued in the field of mathematics and in science in general, as well as in certain industrial laboratory processes. In these activities the dedication to and obsession with absolute accuracy may enhance a person's professional status. However, while these characteristics are virtues under some circumstances, they may become pitfalls and serious obstacles when the desired accuracy is unobtainable. Since this is the situation in most areas of human knowledge, one must be prepared to compromise with the ideal in terms of what is attainable. When one is unable to accept anything short of perfection and becomes anxious, ineffective, and disorganized unless perfection can be achieved, he presents obsessional behavior which, in the extreme, is neurotic and self-defeating.

The obsessional researcher will find himself greatly handicapped, particularly in the social sciences, if he tries to apply absolutes when only approximations are possible. He may find himself being more congenial to the mathematical or measurable aspects of his research project rather than to the broader intuitive and speculative aspects of the problem. The insistence on preciseness when only approximations are possible may often produce such severe anxieties that the effectiveness of a brilliant worker can be reduced to a point where his skill becomes a handicap. The withdrawn or autistic obsessional can often find a suitable outlet for his fantasizing and delusional thinking if he focuses it on painting, dancing, composing, or acting.

In the more practical aspects of living, obsessional patterns can impose many obstacles. While philosophizing and keeping an open mind are admirable goals, there are frequent occasions when rapid decisions must be made without the intellectual consideration of all possible issues. The indecisive obsessional tends to be clumsy, inept, and ineffective in his routine living. He may move slowly and cautiously, delaying all his living while he considers alternative actions.

For truly creative activities one must achieve a balance. Some questions are held open and at the same time answers may be suggested even before all the data are accumulated. To the extent that one is restrained from committing oneself or taking wild leaps without proper guarantees, one might be handicapped in such enterprises. Creativity is characterized by intuitive and premature excursions into areas in which there are no road maps or prior pathways.

The indiscriminate demand for complete certainty can be the cause of an enormous waste of time and energy in tracking down all the factors involved in a phenomenon. The obsessional's ability to be precise and to respect order and routine can make him an asset to any organization. On the other hand, his rigid, inflexible way of operating can quickly irritate and antagonize the less rule-bound, free-wheeling worker. It is clear that in the normal utilization of obsessional patterns some patterns are useful (i.e., productive and adaptive) and others are not. Simply to label a characteristic obsessive or compulsive does not ordinarily convey its positive or constructive elements. However, in delineating the group of normal utilizers of obsessional defenses from the group we say possesses obsessional personality or the obsessional-neurotic group, we must take into account the adaptive as well as the maladaptive aspects of the behavior. What are the distinctions of the obsessional personality group as opposed to the obsessional neurotic group?

The scientific worker who has obsessional patterns can function effectively and constructively if his working conditions are ideal. If his anxiety increases he may have some difficulty in continuing, but he can still make the necessary decisions to proceed with his job. At this time he might be classified in the obsessional personality group. While he is more distressed than the non-symptomatic scientist, he is not nearly so handicapped as the obsessional neurotic who can no longer take effective action. Here the capacity to make a decision is disrupted by the demands for absolute certainty, which is not achievable. Panic and disorganization may follow.

OBSESSIONAL PERSONALITY

Differentiating between manifestations of obsessional traits of behavior and an obsessional personality is a matter of consistency and the extent of the pattern's involvement with the individual's total life. While admittedly such a distinction is extremely difficult to make, it is nevertheless worth the effort. The label "obsessional personality" refers to a widespread, fairly cohesive set of obsessional traits in a person whose anxieties are noticeable. Such behavior patterns are fixed and durable, and one can predict with some degree of accuracy the individual's response to certain stimuli. The consistency of behavior suggests more integrated functioning than is generally found in the occasional bits of obsessional behavior which might occur in any personality structure —such as the hysterical, the schizoid, or the psychopathic personality.

A further distinction between the obsessional personality and the obsessional neurotic is in the area of differing functional capacity. As long as the individual remains productive—though he might be given to fairly extensive rituals or other obsessive behavior—he is not necessarily neurotic. The label "neurotic" refers not only to a clinical syndrome characterized by specific, definable limits, but also to behavior which becomes maladaptive or runs counter to the community's standard for what is acceptable. The individual might behave strangely or impress some people as being odd, but as long as he is integrated and functioning effectively (strictly speaking), he is not neurotic in the public eye. For example, a middle-aged man who held a high fiscal post in a municipal government was involved in endless rituals and obsessional thinking. His favorite preoccupation during World War II was to work out techniques for helping servicemen sublimate their sexual needs. He had devised a sublimation dance in which every male had two females. He also had a project for solving the housing shortage by proposing spatial housing. This was an ingenious proposal in which rockets would be used not only to propel the materials to build the apartments outside the pull of gravity but also to project the inhabitants from the earth to their homes in outer space and back. While he was fully occupied with plans for these programs, his colleagues were unaware of the bizarre nature of his inner life. It was not until he had decided to present these ideas to the President that he, himself, became aware of the peculiarity of his thoughts. He functioned effectively at his job and only when his anxieties became extreme did he need to see a psychiatrist. It was quite clear, at that time, that he was a severely obsessional neurotic, bordering on and periodically regressing into schizophrenia.

It is common to find severely obsessional persons functioning effectively in settings in which their "queerness" and unconventional attitudes may be noticed by all. Either because of the sympathetic good will of the management and colleagues, or because of such people's value to the organization—where they are generally regarded as good workers—they are maintained on the job. It is only when some extreme untoward event occurs or some personal crisis unfolds to aggravate their obsessional patterns that these obsessionals may be dismissed.

Such an instance was true in the case of an electronics engineer who was a totally undisciplined worker. He would arrive at and depart from his plant according to his own schedule, and on many occasions he would work through the night. He was meticulously precise, and had some hand-washing compulsions as well as a total inability to settle for anything less than a perfect performance at the job. While his lack of discipline tended to disrupt the laboratory routine, the management was extremely sympathetic and even managed to increase his hourly rate in order to bring his salary up to a subsistence level. Periodically his preciseness and passion for order would resolve some hitherto unsolvable circuitry problem. However, as his undisciplined behavior began to be too disruptive and his unique qualities less available because of his absence from the job, he was urged to see a psychiatrist.

Shortly after his marriage his performance became more erratic and unreliable. As his professional behavior became more extreme, his performance on the job became markedly disruptive and maladaptive. What heretofore had been considered merely odd and queer was now labelled an obsessional neurosis that required therapy.

Another example is that of a mathematician whose job did not require him to punch a timeclock or to follow a set routine. However, he was expected periodically to file a report on the current status of his project. He worked in a large "think" factory with a great number of brilliant scientists and technicians. While he was considered to be unusually talented and was respected by his superiors, he began to grow panicky about his failure to complete a report which was six months overdue. His indecisiveness and procrastination made it impossible for him to complete the task. While such difficulties were evident in every aspect of his life, he had managed a fairly successful career until he was hired by this high-level scientific laboratory. His anxiety about perfect performances interfered with what he was capable of doing; as his panic increased, his level of performance decreased. He came to therapy on his own volition, finally acknowledging that his indecisiveness was too extreme to be rationalized even as scientific caution. While he managed to postpone his job crisis through repeated promises, his inability to get the report written finally resulted in his being asked to resign.

Manifestations of more-than-"normal" obsessiveness may be subtle or obvious and there may be recognizable rituals of a sufficiently bizarre nature so that the person may be known as an "odd ball," a queer fellow, or an eccentric. In the obsessive personality the rituals may be minimal and known only to the person's intimates, or they may be sufficiently evident to others. At times the obsessional's preoccupations may not be noticed as unusual on casual contact, and only long acquaintance may reveal a piece of obsessional behavior. While the obsessional personality is consistent in using obsessional techniques, the individual retains some flexibility and can function without the undue anxiety that would incapacitate the obsessional neurotic.

OBSESSIONAL NEUROSIS

As the obsessional personality's anxiety increases because of external demands or inner stress, the patterns tend to become more extensive and prominent. The extension of obsessional processes is related to the increasing anxiety as well as to the capacity of the existing patterns to deal with them. While heretofore many of his preoccupations or bizarre bits of behavior could be kept isolated or under control, he now can no longer maintain such control and gradually his activities may be dominated by his compulsions. The islands of activity outside of compulsive pressure tend to become smaller and his rituals may be more evident and less answerable to justification or rationalization. His obsessional activities may become so preoccupying that he has little time for the more routine activities in his living. His work suffers as well as his personal life, and the efforts to isolate his difficulties are less successful. Even though his disabilities are becoming more public—possibly obvious to any bystander—there still remain some successful modes of functioning (except for the most severe neurotic), which often allow him to keep at his job and to remain outside of the mental hospital.

However, as the rigid adherence to his obsessional demands begins to alienate him from his professional colleagues or family unit, the necessity for some psychiatric intervention becomes clear.

Yet the question of therapy is still unclear. When does obsessional behavior require psychiatric intervention? In the extremes the answer is obvious. However, more often the question can be answered only after a consideration of the effects of these patterns on others as well as on the patient. When his effectiveness at his job is grossly impaired or when the symptoms produce sufficient social problems, the need for treatment may become quite evident to his associates. At other times the obsessional preoccupations and hypochondriacal concern with somatic difficulties may be so debilitating that the person himself seeks some relief from these inner torments.

The obsessional often resorts to therapy on his own, in spite of the blow to his pride in such an admission of vulnerability and imperfection. His request for assistance is an admission of imperfection and is made with great reluctance. His awareness of increasing anxiety in the face of some minor crisis and the ensuing panicky expectation of doom makes him fearful of a possible breakdown in his obsessional defenses. At other times he comes to therapy because he feels ineffective, harassed by his compulsions, and not free to make choices or decisions in any area of his life. He recognizes that he is not utilizing his potentialities and that too much energy goes into the planning and programming of his life. He feels incapable of enjoying himself, and too alienated from his family and friends. He may acknowledge that he has no real commitments, even though he may work most intensely and conscientiously. He feels that something is wrong which he cannot clearly verbalize and that he is not getting out of life what is possible, both personally and professionally. Or the bizarre nature of his rituals may become so discomforting and embarrassing that he wishes to eliminate them. It is these subjective factors which are largely responsible for his seeking therapy, and not pressures from the outside. He has a feeling of loss of identity or a feeling of never having had one, and he hopes that therapy will help him find this. The identity problems which characterize obsessional living are the basis for the large number of people visiting psychiatrists in the last three decades. The feeling of unproductiveness coupled with an uncertainty of what one is or wishes to be is a characteristic complaint. These factors, rather than severe anxieties, are the main instigators for therapy as the obsessional defenses are very successful in maintaining anxiety at a low level.

Many obsessional neurotics and people with obsessional personalities come to therapy because of psychosomatic difficulties. Ulcers, colitis, and cardiovascular complications are common; the patients, after thorough examination by an internist, are often informed that their problems are functional and require psychiatric care. This is extremely difficult for them to accept, since it not only implies a weakness but also means that treatment will be long, arduous, and will require their participation.

A young man of 39 was referred for therapy by his general practitioner after prolonged study of cardiac complaints for a period of three years—with repeated EKG studies, blood and kidney tests, and innumerable X-rays. The heart condition began when the patient awoke one evening with palpitations and a feeling of pain in his chest. He immediately assumed that he had heart disease and would not move until the arrival of the doctor, who confirmed the patient's worst suspicions by saying that he had a heart murmur. For three years he cut down his activity to a minimum, gave up all sports (indoors and out), and became preoccupied with observing his heart action under all sorts of circumstances. Prior to this difficulty, however, he had many other troubles because of his indecisive procrastinations. He had numerous phobias which involved closed spaces, open spaces, automobiles, bridges, elevators, etc. His living was enormously circumscribed by rituals of all sorts, particularly relating to his health, and he had cut out all social relationships, both male and female, because they might be a drain on his heart. He insisted that he had heart disease, and that he could die at any moment. The thorough medical study, which unfortunately served to fix many of his obsessional preoccupations, proved to be negative and his physician decided that the tachycardia was psychological in origin and that the murmur had no physiological significance. The young man visited a psychiatrist, but could not accept the psychological explanation of his condition. His obsessional difficulties were clearly manifest to the psychiatrist, but they did not impress the patient—or his physician; it was only the somatic complaints that produced the referral. It was easier for the patient to accept therapy for some medical or physiological need rather than for psychological difficulties. This is understandable when we recognize that the obsessional person believes that physical illnesses are outside of his control but that mental illnesses are entirely within his control; therefore it is his own fault or weakness that produces it. Heart disease is thought to occur without his intervention, and he is able to believe that he has done nothing to bring it about. Emotional problems, however, are assumed to be the result of a lazy, undisciplined, and selfish concern for himself. While this attitude has a grain of truth, it is exaggerated in the typical obsessional style so that physical illness is considered good and mental illness bad. The physician can do something for his patient in treating a physical illness, but in a mental illness the patient must do it himself and the treatment is slow, painstaking, and without magical cures. This may account for the obsessional's ready acknowledgment of physical illnesses in contrast to his reluctant recognition of emotional problems. It also explains why many obsessional patients may come to therapy for their ulcers or their colitis—but will not see the need for getting help for their extreme indecisiveness or procrastination.

   To summarize: all people use obsessional techniques in their living. The extent to which these defenses take over the person's total living or interfere with one's productivity, or make one appear to be odd and curious, will determine the label applied. It is not only the extent of the activities which are involved in obsessional behavior but also the capacity of the rest of the organism to isolate that behavior and still function effectively. As one's adjustment and adaptation become less successful and the obsessional living more noticeable, the label of "obsessional neurosis" becomes applicable. Therapy is determined not by label or the presence of obsessional behavior, but by the extent to which the person's living is blocked—both subjectively and objectively.

PART   II

the obsessive
state and
other syndromes

CHAPTER 5

Depression

In the preceding chapters the obsessional mechanism has been described as a defense against feelings of powerlessness and helplessness. What happens when the obsessional devices fail to serve their purpose and the person is forced to acknowledge his weakness and his incapacity to control all the aspects of his living? A number of possibilities confront him, ranging from the need to extend or expand his obsessional defenses to a total breakdown of his integrative capacities. A frequent outcome of the failure of an obsessional defense is a depressive reaction. In this framework depression is not viewed as a specific defense or a syndrome but rather as a response to the breakdown of a defense mechanism.

Until very recently depression has been described as a disease entity. This fact is related to the historical development of psychiatric theory out of the medical tradition of separate disease entities with differing etiologies. While this procedure was entirely rational for disorders in which the pathologic changes were demonstrable and the causative agents identifiable, attempts to use such criteria with mental disorders proved inaccurate and misleading. Except where the etiology was clear and established (e.g., GPI caused by syphilis or senile arteriosclerosis), the attempts to establish disease entities out of symptom complexes have been unsuccessful.

A great advance in psychiatric nomenclature took place when the hundred or more presumed functional disorders were classified under these major headings: the neuroses and the psychoses which consisted of the schizophrenic and manic-depressive disorders. While this step encouraged the movement away from discrete disease entities, it still mantained the notion of a single disease with a specific cause and treatment. This tendency still plagues psychiatric theory and therapy and has resulted in serious errors in appraising the value of certain therapeutic measures such as shock or drug therapy. In addition, it has led to a search for etiological agents which has sidetracked psychiatric research for a long time. It has also been responsible for much mischief in statistical studies of the therapeutic results of psychotherapy, as it presumes to deal with established and clear-cut disease entities. Some of the presumed disease entities may simply be reaction modes or adaptive techniques designed to cope with certain intrapsychic or environmental stresses.

Recent contributions to psychiatric theory have approached mental illness from this latter framework, which emphasizes the adaptive activities of human behavior. Such a viewpoint focuses on the needs of the individual and the processes and activities that are set into motion to fulfill these needs. If the needs are excessive, extreme, or distorted, the behavior that is organized to fill them may be maladaptive and may fail to satisfy the individual's productive requirements. Such responses are called neurotic or psychotic and they constitute a wide range of reaction types which are called defense mechanisms. At times these mechanisms cluster into large reaction types suited to deal with particular demands of the organisms. While they may resemble disease entities because their manifestations are similar, they do not constitute separate syndromes with specific etiology, pathology, or therapeutic management.

The understanding of depression has suffered from this historical development, particularly since it has been viewed as a disorder based upon physiological or biochemical causes. Despite the consistent biochemical changes in amine and ketosteroid metabolism, as well as salts such as potassium chloride, depression cannot be viewed as a disorder of metabolism. Since it is such a widespread phenomenon and is present to degrees in almost everyone, it is more likely to be a response of the organism to some external stimulus which registers in a biochemical fashion in the cells. Depression is not something one *has*, but rather it is something that is *happening* in a person in relation to another person. The chemical changes are probably secondary.

This likelihood is most strikingly manifested by the massive reactions in Voodoo death, when "the word" can produce adrenal insufficiency and death and when forgiveness from the chief can produce an immediate and striking improvement in the dying person. This reaction is certainly a psychological one and represents a reaction to disapproval or total rejection in a social setting in which such beliefs are held. It is, incidentally, a dramatic representation of the power of words and provides a major clue to the efficacy of psychotherapy in the depressive disorder.

CONCEPTS OF DEPRESSION

Freud's earlier classifications of the mental disorders was strongly influenced by Kraepelin. In spite of their more dynamic explanation, Kraepelin's writings supported the notion of depression as being a distinct disease entity with a specific etiology and therapy. Since Kraepelin, however, there has been a recurring tendency to link depression with the obsessional state. Premorbid obsessional personality traits are particularly common in involutional depression.

Freud's formulation was related to the libido theory and stated that depression was the result of the loss of an ambivalent loved object. He felt that the individual introjected the lost object and that the hostility manifested in this disorder resulted from the expression of the person's feeling toward the hated aspects of the lost object. This interpretation was useful in explaining many observable manifestations of the depressive reaction, both neurotic and psychotic. It emphasized the elements of hostility and the loss of a valued object, which resembled the process of mourning. It was particularly useful in increasing the understanding of suicide, and it served to draw some focus away from the physiological theories which emphasized biochemical and hormonal elements. However, in retaining the disease concept, the viewpoint discouraged the exploration of depression as an adaptive reaction which attempted to restore some lost possession—whether it be a person or thing. Later theorists such as Edith Weigert, Karen Horney, and Sandor Rado helped to expand the earlier dynamic formulations, although they disagreed about the omnipresence of hostility and its major role in the depressive process. The emphasis on oral factors in the disorder, as highlighted by Karl Abraham, was also discounted. While Freud focused on the "lost object" (which referred to a person), Rado viewed the loss in terms of a loss of love; he saw the depressive reaction as an attempt to restore that loss.

The concept of depression which is presented here proposes that depression is a reaction to a loss *and* is a maladaptive response in attempting to repair the loss. It is not seen as a disease, but as a potential in all personality structures when a loss is experienced as leaving one totally helpless and impotent. It is in this respect that its relationship to the obsessional mechanism is manifested: it is under these circumstances that the obsessional mechanisms break down because of internal or external stresses.

A variety of defensive responses may occur in the wake of a failing obsessional defense—e.g., schizophrenia, paranoid developments, and other grandiose states, as well as depression. At present it is extremely difficult to determine why one response occurs and not another. However, it is clear that the depressive reaction is commonplace because the obsessional mode of behavior is universal. The depressive reaction may be mild or severe, with the same wide spectrum as noted in the previous chapter. When it occurs in the normal obsessional or in those with any other neurotic disorder or personality type it is the failure of the obsessional defense to maintain the standards or values considered by the individual to be essential. Depression follows the conviction or apprehension that the value, person, or thing which is deemed necessary may actually be lost or no longer available.

These values or persons are not necessarily realistic nor are the demands reasonable. They are invariably extreme and excessive and form part of the obsessive neurotic value system in which the requirements for perfection and omniscience are essential ingredients. While the obsessional system is intact, the illusion of omniscience and perfection can be maintained. However, a crisis, a sudden disease, or some unexpected event may stir up the individual's apprehension about his ability to maintain these standards. If the concerns continue and the apprehension becomes a conviction, depression may supervene.

The relationship of the obsessional dynamism to depression is frequently portrayed in a dramatic form in the involutional depressions that arise in retired or incapacitated people. The precipitating factor is the forced recognition that one's previous productivity and capacity has become limited. This exacerbates any prior obsessional or perfectionistic traits, obsessional preoccupation, doubting, or procrastination—coupled with depressive reactions about not being able to live up to one's previous standards.

A prototype of this situation is represented by a 62-year-old lawyer who had been very successful in his profession, and who had to slow down his pace for the past five years because of a heart attack. Although he had been the organizer of a very successful law firm, he had over the past few years become increasingly depressed, with feelings of worthlessness and despair.

He was, in his own words, a perfectionist, who was dedicated to his job and would not settle for anything but the best. He had few other interests, and tried to acquire *all* the knowledge about his particular specialty. He was inflexible in his demands upon himself and simply had to keep up with the best. Though he had achieved a large measure of success and was happily married, he was a tense, anxious person.

In trying to slow down at work, he began to feel less adequate than his colleagues, and guilty about not earning his way. He needed extra assurances about his output and his usefulness to the firm, while his colleagues tried to relieve him of difficult problems. He began to notice that he tired more easily and could not keep up with the younger staff in long-winded conferences which involved extensive drinking. He could not accept the realities of the aging process, and was humiliated when he felt tired. He was compelled to try to prove that his efficiency was as high as ever—even though he was aware of his physiological limitations.

As he slowly began to feel depressed, he began wondering whether the firm would drop him in spite of his having participated in its founding. He felt he was a failure and wondered if he had a right to burden others. He began to assume some paranoid ideas. His sex life was less active, and he wondered if his wife would also abandon him. At this point, his depression was still mild, but it was clear that it would not be long before he might be involved in suicidal preoccupations or even in possible attempts at suicide.

The picture he described was directly related to his inability to accept the inevitable consequences of physiological aging, with its psychological accompaniments. By activity, success, and continuous acknowledgement from others he could avoid the full recognition of his failing capacities. The heart attack forced this recognition upon him, as well as a recognition of his dependence upon others. He was forced to admit that being 62 years of age was different from being 40. As the recognition of his increasing limitations was forced upon him, he became depressed, despaired of the future, and saw no reason for existence. He concluded that he would have to go out and get a new batch of clients to prove that he was as good as ever—but he realized that this was not possible. He could not recognize that aging is inevitable and must be dealt with as a fact of life.

It is abundantly clear that a heretofore successfully adapted obsessional individual was, under forced circumstances of aging and disease, unable to accept his human predicament. He could only react with despair, hopelessness, and depression.

Depression is, of course, hardly confined to older people! The demand for perfection often causes a student to become depressed if he fails to maintain his demands for "A" grades in all subjects. His presumed failure convinces him of his fallibility and his depression is a response to the feeling of loss of standards and values. This is also the case when a person receives a promotion and an increase in authority and reacts with a contradictory depressive response. At such times his neurotic expectation to be loved by all may be shattered by the realization that his promotion requires him to be a disciplinarian and perhaps an unpopular figure.

The object or value that is supposed to be lost is considered essential; it may be the cornerstone of the neurotic integration which is endangered if it is lost.

Depression occurs only in response to the neurotic elements in a person's personality and is often the key that allows us to see these elements. The loss of real things tends to produce a determined effort to replace what has been lost. Depression is the neurotic's maladaptive response which attempts to *force* the return of the lost object or value.

CASE ILLUSTRATIONS

This situation was dramatically portrayed in an extremely bright and ambitious young man. His expectations far exceeded his realistic potentials, which led to several severe depressive reactions while at college. In the early part of his marriage he became depressed when he felt that his wife was losing interest in him, and this caused him to seek psychoanalytic therapy. During the treatment process he went into another severe depression, which permitted us to study the process's development in detail. It began after he became the director of a national organization which was faltering until he began making a notable success of it. He inaugurated a large fund drive, he was in excellent spirits, and he functioned most effectively—even though his standards were extremely high and he was overly dedicated and conscientious. As the fund drive grew more elaborate and the deadline for a major event in the drive was approaching, he became overwhelmed by the details. He tried to handle every phase of the venture himself and demanded that every activity be perfectly executed. He wanted guarantees that the gala evening that was planned would come off perfectly. As evidence began to accumulate that it would be successful and as more prominent persons became involved, he became more depressed instead of being reassured. The participation of all these important people made it even more imperative that it be successful, and he demanded further guarantees that all would go perfectly.

As the day approached he became increasingly agitated and preoccupied. His restlessness and insomnia were stimulated by a constant reexamination of all the plans. All the minutiae became major issues and every phase had to be scrutinized anew to prevent some disaster from occurring. What had begun as a successful venture which he was handling effectively turned into a nightmare of fear and danger. He saw himself on trial—as if the event would determine his entire future standing. Its significance was enormously exaggerated. He saw himself in the spotlight, critically appraised by all, which justified his concerns and perfectionistic strivings. He became self-critical, self-derogatory, and had crying spells—with demands for reassurance about impossible matters. His physical processes slowed down, which aggravated his depression further, until he was no longer able to get to the office. Although he withdrew several weeks before

the event, it still came off well. He felt guilty about his failure
to complete the project, but he received much acclaim for its
success. His depression now quickly lifted. The whole incident
was strikingly similar to a depression he suffered several years
earlier when he was learning to drive. His expectations about his
driving skill after a few lessons made the driver's test so distressing
that he abandoned it for fear he would look ridiculous. Since he
did not feel completely in control of the car and anticipated a
debacle, he gave up driving altogether.

On both these occasions his depression was directly in response to the increasing obsessional demands which he made upon
himself. As he became aware of this he was overwhelmed by
feelings of failure and tragedy and his illusionary requirements of
omnipotence and perfection began to be shattered. Despair and
hopelessness were the result. The understanding and the resolution of the depressive process strengthened his feelings of esteem
and lessened his obsessional requirements. This was facilitated by
his recognition of the success of the venture which was the result
of his own efforts and which succeeded without guarantees of
perfection.

Comments

The effect of a loss of a highly esteemed value or person
upon one who is not involved in a neurotic personality structure
is different from depression; it is more like the process of mourning. The individual quickly attempts to reorganize his personality
structure without the lost value or person. While some grief
normally accompanies this process, there is a reasonable effort to
replace the loss or substitute something else.

This is contrary to Freud's view that mourning and melancholia are similar with the exception that the loss in depression
or melancholia is unconscious while in grief or mourning it is
conscious. It seems to me, however, that this distinction is not
valid; in depression, too, the loss may often be conscious. Mourning and depression are similar with respect to the emotion of

unhappiness which is prominent in both states. Mourning is a constructive process which follows a loss in which the relationship was primarily one of tenderness and love. Mourning is also a process of repair, which enables the person to sever and terminates his relationship. In this process his esteem for the lost person may be enhanced and he may benefit from an intensified identification with him. The mourner's personality may be reintegrated at a higher level of maturity, and the experience may ultimately be a productive one.

Melancholia, on the other hand, is a destructive process in which the person refuses to relinquish the lost person and refuses to accept the loss as a reality. It is experienced as abandonment, and the person feels helpless and impotent. There is a marked diminution in self-esteem, with self-derogatory and self-deprecatory accusations. The individual senses an attack on his pride, and he feels worthless and self-destructive. He resents the loss and feels antagonistic toward those who have deprived him. This often results in considerable hostility, overtly expressed as threats or attacks (both verbal and physical) or covertly expressed in the form of nagging, demanding, pleading, and clinging. This is part of the depressed person's effort to repair the loss by forcing others to return what has been lost. The demands are generally made upon those who are closest and most intimate with the depressed person. Ultimately, the demands may extend to the whole environment in an attempt to force people to restore or reinstate the former condition. This is essentially a *power* operation and a struggle to control the behavior of others. The behavioral manifestations may be mild or severe, overt or covert, passive sullenness or active clinging, or accusing and demanding. They are essentially energetic efforts at restoring that which has been lost. The self-destructive tendencies are the most powerful weapons in this effort.

In view of the central role played by control and power in the obsessional mechanism, we should expect to find a close relationship of the depressions with the obsessional states. This similarity has been noted by a great many personality theorists—be-

ginning with Freud and Karl Abraham, and including Karen
Horney, Harry Stack Sullivan, Franz Alexander, and Sandor
Rado. Their descriptions of the depressive personality are almost
identical to that of the obsessive-compulsive personality. Franz
Alexander noted the similarity and attempted to make some
distinction between the two. He described the depressive personality as a warm and practical one which showed preferences for
concrete rather than abstract thinking. The compulsive, on the
other hand, is inclined toward abstract thinking and remains
largely detached from his fellow man. However, such distinctions
are not sufficiently specific to warrant typing separate personality
structures. The compulsive personality is often practical and
frequently concrete, while the depressive's warmth is often like
the compulsive's strong attachments at the extremes of feeling.
It is likely that what has been described as a separate depressive
personality is actually an obsessional personality that tends toward
depressive reactions.

The depressive person is described by Franz Alexander and
others as one who has exceptionally high standards and who
cannot accept any compromises. He is egocentric and over-
reacts to frustration and denial. His relationship to others is
characterized as one of exploitative dependency, in which he
controls and manipulates others. He tends to deal in extremes of
good and bad (black and white) and fails to see the total person,
who is a mixture of both. He is serious, dedicated, and determined
to achieve perfection in all things. He feels that he has failed to
fulfill his own expectations of himself, as well as his parents.'
However, he maintains his level of existence by an illusion that
he is achieving a perfect performance. When he is forced by
circumstances to acknowledge some deficiency or failure in his
system of values, he feels humiliated by the notion that he has
lost status and esteem in the eyes of others. This is accompanied
by feelings of hopeless despair and depression. This description is
a precise parallel of the descriptions of obsessionals who react with
despair to any awareness of imperfections. When the failure is
extreme and presumed to be irreparable, a severe depression may

ensue. If the obsessional feels that total rejection may follow some failure on his part to maintain absolute control at all times, depression may also follow. As the excessive and exaggerated standards of the obsessional defense can rarely be maintained, it is inevitable that frequent depressions will occur—ranging from the mild to the severe forms.

ONSET OF DEPRESSION

Depression not only results from the failure to maintain excessive standards, but may also result when one anticipates that weakness or deficiencies will prevent one from even approximating such standards. The situation may be transient, and may be relieved when some evidence of acceptability or some success in an unrelated area temporarily restores the illusion of perfection. Since the obsessional person has inconsistent and fleeting feelings of self-worth, he cannot appraise his capabilities with validity— hence his assets are easily overlooked in moments of temporary difficulty and despair.

Such a situation is very common in neurotic states, particularly in the obsessional personality. It may also occur in other personality structures in which obsessional factors are significant, the frequency being directly related to the amount of obsessional defenses in the persons' personality patterns.

It is this view of the dynamics of depression that enables us to see why such reactions are so widespread. Since we all utilize obsessional defenses, it is small wonder that most of us experience frequent and minor depressions in the course of living. At times it is quite evident that the issue of standards is related to the onset of depression—for example, when minor or trivial events trigger the reaction. When an extreme reaction takes place because one has received a lower grade than expected, it is evident that the response cannot be fully understood in terms of this event alone. It would be better understood if one could realize the severe condemnation and utter contempt which the person feels for himself because he failed to fulfill his demands. His response is so marked that he anticipates total rejection and severe censure from others. When success brings on a depression, the same factors are at work. The person who has a depressed reaction to success aspires to higher standards and values than those expressed in his new status. His underlying feelings of inadequacy and his demands for a perfect performance in his new position leave him with feelings of uncertainty and incapacity to achieve them. If the apprehension is great enough, it may bring on a depression. Success in such instances is not regarded as a mark of achievement but rather as a test and a challenge toward further achievement. Thus success produces tension and uneasiness instead of a comfortable feeling of recognition and acknowledgement.

This concept of depression demonstrates that it is more than a faulty process of past learning; it is more likely related to what is happening in the present and to anticipations of the future. This view also provides a significant clue to the treatment of depression and the necessity of focusing on the here and now and not to become obsessively preoccupied with the past.

DYNAMICS OF DEPRESSION

Freud's description of depression, amplified by Karl Abraham and others, focused on the hostile elements in the process—i.e., the tendency to express one's anger toward the ambivalent, introjected love object. This produced the typical picture of the depression—with guilt, self-accusations and self-destructive tendencies. Suicide was held to be the extreme instance of the depressive tendency toward self-hatred. These explanations required the death-instinct and libido hypotheses.

From the adaptational point of view (without recourse to earlier theories), depression is a reparative process which supervenes when a person feels he has lost something vital to his psychic integration. The reaction of despair and depression is the result of the anticipated rebuff and the expectation of total rejection as a consequence of this loss. With this framework in mind, the other elements in depression become more understandable. The hostile, demanding, and clinging behavior is related to this desperate attempt to regain the lost object from those felt to be responsible for taking it away or capable of restoring it. The depressed person pleads, begs, demands, cajoles, and attempts to *force* the environment to replace or restore the object.

At first the tenacious and demanding behavior stirs up sympathy, pity, and sometimes even empathy. But as these reactions do not restore what has been lost, the demands increase and then produce resentment and anger toward the depressed person. The end result is an annoyed and distressed individual who generally feels guilty, even though he has tried his best to please and appease the depressed person. The annoyance soon turns to noticeable irritation and finally to anger. At this point the depressed individual may actually be rejected; this confirms his grievances, which in turn produces hostility and justifies his accusations against the environment.

Unlike the above-described agitated type of depressive, who hopes that by evoking guilt reactions he can stir up some activity in his behalf, the silent, retarded depressive is immovable and uncommunicative—conveying a silent rebuke and reproach to the environment. He may refuse to eat or to participate in any activities whatsoever. The passive, seemingly demanding attitude is actually a most potent device in inciting large amounts of guilt and activity. All efforts of friends, relatives, and other helpers are received with only slight appreciation because they fail to fulfill the depressed person's demands. There is always a note of criticism about the limitations and inadequacy of what is being done for him. One soon begins to feel that it is impossible to satisfy the depressed individual and begins to resist his demands. The immediate family and friends are the first to be alienated, even though they begin by being the most understanding. This situation soon spreads to others, often including the physician and psychiatrist.

Then the depressive's hostility becomes more evident and a vicious circle is quickly established. His hostile attacks stimulate counterattacks; he is accused of being insatiable, greedy, and ungrateful—which only increases his hostility. Much of the symptomatology of the depressed person reflects an attempt to regain control of himself by desperately trying to regain the lost object. The typical obsessional picture, with its devices and techniques for achieving control, can be clearly seen in the behavior of the depressed individual.

Within this framework the problem of suicide and some of the contradictory elements in the older theories of depression can be clarified. While it has been known for some time that suicide is particularly prevalent in depressive states, it was not directly proportional to the depth of the depression or the extent of the expressed or repressed hostility. As a matter of fact, suicide often occurs when the depression is at a minimum or moving toward some resolution. It also seems to occur when the overt hostility is greater than the covert hostility—in contradiction to the theoretical presumption. On the other hand, suicide is directly related to the degree of despair and the feeling of hopelessness about being able to restore one's esteem in the face of expected condemnation from the community. The threat of such action is therefore greatest as one goes into or out of a depression, i.e., when the despair about reconstructing one's former status and integration is greatest. Suicide seems to be unrelated to the amount of hostility; instead, it seems to be directly related to feelings of hopelessness. Oversimplified notions of suicide as a means of embarrassing others or expressing hostility toward them seems no longer to be tenable.

COMMENTS ON TREATMENT

The solution to the dilemma created by the conflict between pleading for help and rejecting it as being "patronizing" lies in giving help judiciously and wisely—with a view to stimulating the greatest feeling of esteem without stirring up major resentments. This requires some knowledge of the depressive's behavior patterns so as not to respond unwisely to his neurotic and contradictory demands.

The demand to be entirely independent underlies much of the depressive's behavior. The depression is an appeal for a meaningful relationship and is, in essence, a cry for love which cannot be made openly and unashamedly. Such a person has difficulty in developing a loving relationship through care, concern, interest, and affection. He has the obsessional conception that love means being weak and giving in. He tries to force love through demands that produce guilt feelings in others. While others may initially respond with loving concern, the continued ungrateful attitude of the depressed person ultimately changes the love to irritation and anger. Anger and frustration may also occur in the therapeutic situation as a result of such maneuvers. It may become very difficult for the therapist to restrain his own hostility.

Coercive, insistent demands and angry rebukes antagonize the environment. This is precisely what takes place in the obsessional mechanism. However, the obsessional's loss is not experienced as real; therefore the dynamic patterns are still concerned with maintaining control rather than retrieving a loss. There are no demands and rebukes for restoration of control, as the obsessional individual still believes that he is maintaining control. It is when there is a *conviction* of loss—whether real or imagined, conscious or out-of-awareness—that the depressive maneuver supervenes in the obsessional's attempt to replace the loss.

The relationship of mania to depression—which is manifest in manic-depressive disorders and related states—can also be more clearly understood in the context of the depression's being related to the obsessive-compulsive dynamism. At times the depressive maneuvers appear to produce a restoration of the lost object or value. This, however, is not real or valid; it is impossible to replace the lost object or to restore the impossible requirements of the individual. The feeling of success is magical—

an illusionary fulfillment not visible to others. The depressed person's reaction to such an event is one of joy and satisfaction, which in an extreme state is called mania, since it confirms his belief in his magical powers and his capacity to control and manipulate the world for his purposes. While such a reaction is generally short-lived, it is a state of euphoria in which all forms of power and skills are artificially assumed and the person acts as if he were possessed of omnipotent and omniscient qualities. He claims the capacity to achieve anything and everything. It is a state of exaggerated grandiosity in which there is a limitless view of one's physical and mental capacities. However, failure to recognize one's limitations (even in the manic state) can also bring about a depression, as in the cyclic disorders of depression and mania. Mania may relate to the omnipotence and magical powers which the obsessive-compulsive seeks.

A striking example of the relationship of depression, mania, grandiosity, and paranoid developments occurred in a young lady who, after 13 years of a rather stormy marriage, was finally faced with the possibility of divorce. While this issue had been raised previously, she was certain at those times that her husband would not leave her. On the last occasion he informed her in clear and decisive terms that he was separating on a permanent basis. Her initial reaction was one of depression, with pleas, promises, and resolution to change. When this had no effect upon him she became hyperactive and set about visiting friends and planning for her future. During this period she insisted that her husband really did love her and would ultimately return. She developed delusional ideas about how much her husband loved her, and cited evidence to substantiate it. Any evidence to the contrary was denied and she insisted that what had transpired was in the nature of a test. Her manic behavior persisted for several days, with increasingly grandiose delusions which culminated in a paranoid outburst while she was in a beauty parlor.

On the day which preceded this outbreak she assumed that all the neighbors were on guard in order to make certain that she got all the sleep she needed. She felt that she was a privileged special person and the object of everyone's concern and interest. At the beauty parlor, however, she became abusive and violent—accusing her hairdresser of trying to humiliate and destroy her status in the eyes of her husband. Her behavior became so extreme that she required hospitalization at this time. Within days this delusional system disappeared when she began to accept realistically the estranged situation; she then began to plan how she would win her husband back. She was amused, horrified, and curious about her delusional ideas, but could not adequately explain how they developed.

If depression is related to the obsessive dynamism, then the responsiveness of depressions to physiological therapies must also be accounted for. Because electric shock therapy and drug convulsants produced effects which either injured the patient or made him fearfully resistive, he viewed such treatment as punishment. This attitude coincided with the theory of depression which implied that such people are guilty and self-destructive. Shock therapy was viewed as relieving the super ego of its harshness, permitting the depression to be resolved. This is an appealing view—even though the insulin therapies (unlike metrazol and ECT) are neither painful nor distressing. Too, the use of tranquilizers, psychic energizers, and placebos—which produce little or no distress yet prove to be valuable—casts serious doubts on such an interpretation. It has never been clearly established where the value of such dissimilar physiological approaches lies. The tranquilizing drugs, with their mildly euphoric effect, and the psychic energizers which improve the patient's physical condition, are also beneficial in the treatment of depressive states.

It is generally agreed that it is necessary to produce a confused state before benefit can be derived from many physiologically based procedures. Such confusion is also produced by the tranquillizing drugs. While a severe confused state may not be essential, what does seem to be necessary is a disorganization of the individual's existing value systems. The high standards which have been unfulfilled and the resulting low esteem and self-derogatory accusations are disrupted by these approaches, allowing the individual to reorganize his value systems in a less rigid and extreme fashion. The temporary loss of memory induced by these procedures also permits such a value reorganization—either on a pre-illness basis or on an even more moderate and realistic one. This reorganization, with its reduced demands on the person, results in a rapid amelioration of the depressive symptomatology.

When psychotherapy assists in a reorganization of the distorted values of a depressed person it also facilitates resolution of the difficulty. Shock and drug therapies, by producing confusion, memory defects, or some reduction of the tension involved in maintaining false ideals, can accelerate this process.

In spontaneous recoveries which occur by merely changing the individual's environment, a reorganization of the value system can also be noted. The change of geography, of the interpersonal setting, or of the usual routine of the depressed person often permits him to appraise his value system in the new setting and to discover its false or neurotic basis.

Aside from the physiological approaches, therapy for depression must take into account the factors noted in the relationship of depression to the obsessive-compulsive disorders. The therapeutic problem centers on the recognition of false value systems and the underlying neurotic supports which have been lost, rather than on the issue of hostility and its expression. The power techniques of the person must be exposed for their true intent and purpose and the possibility of establishing a new value system must be introduced. Invariably, the lost object is an exaggerated, overly idealized value or goal which was incapable of ever being actualized in the first place. A revision of such goals will reduce the necessity for maintaining control over and manipulation of the environment, thus eliminating the fear of being rejected or isolated. What is accomplished in the physiological therapies can be more permanently and usefully produced through a psychotherapeutic process that gives full consideration to the dynamics involved. Such a project will undoubtedly serve the patient more effectively because it will not only relieve the depression but will also open up the entire obsessive-compulsive problem for consideration. In view of the high rate of remissions produced by such physiological resolutions, the somewhat slower results produced by the psychotherapeutic process may, in the long run, prove more efficient and economical.

CHAPTER   6

Phobias

To fulfill the goal of maintaining absolute control over oneself and others, one must have the power, intelligence, or ability to predict the future— or one must avoid any situation in which loss of control may occur. I have described the various techniques utilized by the obsessional personality to attempt total mastery through either intelligence or magic. The other alternative—that of avoiding anything which threatens loss of control—is called a phobia. The individual absolutely avoids a situation which is a symbolic representation of the potential danger; he does not avoid the actual danger itself. In this way the phobia is one of the most powerful techniques of defense in the obsessional personality structure.

Phobias attracted the attention of the earliest medical practitioners, but it is only recently that meaningful explanations have been suggested for their presence. The Greeks described many phobias, such as agorophobia and claustrophobia, which names indicated the object of the phobia. Freud became interested in phobias quite early in his career and revised his conception of them many times. In 1895 he wrote a paper on the relationship between obsessions and phobias. In this paper he distinguished between the two by indicating that in phobias the emotional state is always one of morbid anxiety while in the obsessions other emotional states (such as doubt and anger) may occur in the same capacity as fear does in the phobias. He also pointed out that the origin of the phobia was fear and the source was derived from the symbols of unconscious fantasies and conflicts. He said: ". . . I will state that combinations of a phobia and an obsession proper may co-exist and indeed this a very frequent occurrence."

While he maintained this distinction, Freud confused these two categories at various times, classifying them under the rubric of hysteria or the anxiety neuroses. In the famous study of Hans, who had a phobia when he was five years old, Freud emphasized that phobias belonged with the anxiety neuroses, because there was a similarity between the psychological structure of phobias and hysteria. The function of the phobia as an avoidance technique was evident in its very essence. It was this issue that was spotlighted when Freud considered phobia to be a hysterical phenomenon—yet he continued to link phobias with obsessions and, at times, considered them to be almost synonymous. An excerpt from his *Interpretation of Dreams* highlights this attitude: "I had an opportunity of obtaining a profound insight into the unconscious psychic life of a young man for whom an obsessional neurosis made life almost unendurable, so that he could not go into the streets because he was tormented by the fear that he would kill everyone he met. He spent his days in contriving evidence of an alibi in case he should be accused of any murder that might have been committed in the city. After the painful illness and death of his father (to whom he discovered, in analysis, he had murderous impulses) when the young man was in his 31st year the obsessive reproach made its appearance, which transferred itself to strangers in the form of this phobia." Freud added, "Anyone capable of wishing to push his own father from a mountaintop into an abyss cannot be trusted to spare the lives of persons less closely related to him and therefore does well to lock himself into his room." Freud could have added in this case that the phobia was a device to exert and to guarantee the necessary control that would obviate the dangers involved in the patient's going out into the streets. In this brief vignette Freud indicated his psychodynamic theory of phobias and obsessions, and gave an inkling of the two disorders' close association.

The obsessional preoccupations and ritualistic behavior of this patient were a means of controlling the aggressive impulses which had unconscious roots in his hatred of his father. Both the phobia and obsessive devices were attempts to control dangerous and undesirable impulses of a sexual or aggressive nature. While Freud emphasized sexual and aggressive impulses in the development of phobias, *any* "out of control" impulses which would be a threat to the integrity of the individual can be involved. It need not be necessarily a hostile or aggressive impulse. It may develop around tender impulses, power drives, or the need to maintain pride and self-esteem. Loss of control and concern about humiliating and threatening consequences which might result are the factors that produce a phobia. The danger of loss of control does not necessarily involve hostile feelings. Rather, the fear of losing control is in itself the threat of being humiliated and made to feel worthless. It is a public display of inadequacy and imperfection rather than a fear of violence that provides the phobic state.

The phobia, by an absolute injunction, prevents an individual from confronting any situation, place, or person potentially capable of producing anxiety and that may temporarily put the individual out of control. It is a ritualized avoidance reaction which, like all rituals, attempts to exert some control over nature through the agency of magic. The phobia is a ritual of "no doing" or inaction. The obsessive-compulsive syndrome, with its characteristic rituals or behaving or thinking, involves some doing or positive activity to maintain control, thus avoiding the intolerable humiliation which comes from the awareness that he is a mere mortal and imperfect.

AVOIDANCE REACTIONS

The phobia prevents the person from coming into contact with the kind of situation or thing that may put him out of control. However, avoidance reactions must be distinguished from other avoidance tendencies which are prominent in nature; i.e., not all avoidance reactions are phobias. For example, in the typical conditioned responses in man and animals, certain objects or experiences are avoided because of a prior unpleasant experience. These avoidance reactions are specific, literal, and devoid of any content other than the anticipated pain or displeasure based on previous experience and reinforced by subsequent ones. This is implicit in the learning process. It is a physiological response and part of the inherent self-preservation mechanism. Such a response may be reflex in nature or secondarily conditioned. One experience with a cactus plant, or one whiff of ammonia may produce a strong avoidance reaction. On a lesser scale, food reactions and other sensory experiences may condition the person against further contacts.

Other avoidance reactions may not be conditioned by repetitive experiences, but may occur under single, dramatic, and traumatic circumstances—perhaps under circumstances of severe stress, as in times of war. The effect might be a sudden and dramatic avoidance of certain elements in that experience. Such occurrences have been confused with phobias in the past, and even mistakenly labelled as such. These are conditioned responses, whether operant or nonoperant, as opposed to the phobia, which is a defensive reaction based on emotional elements in the experience. The need to distinguish between these responses is not a semantic game or even of only theoretical concern; it is of great practical importance.

An example concerns a pilot who, during a bombing mission, underwent severe danger and was exposed to intense, fear-provoking stimuli. Consequently, he developed extreme fear upon approaching a plane, looking at a plane, or even thinking about flying. This pilot's reaction was based on an actual danger in a situation which produced such discomfort that he refused to confront a similar situation again. The object avoided was directly involved in the experience. There was no symbolism or transformation of the elements involved. It was a rational and comprehensible outcome of an intense experience of anxiety which, while its manifestations resemble a phobia in many ways and may even be a prelude to a phobic reaction, is actually a simple avoidance reaction based on conditioning. The phobia, on the other hand, is a more complicated phenomenon which invariably involves some symbolic transformation and deals with psychic dangers as opposed to physical dangers. Often the avoided dangers may be vague and entirely unrelated to the phobic objects.

If the avoidance reaction described above began to spread so that elevators, heights, and crowds all began to be involved (not just airplanes), it would then move into the realm of the phobia. This often occurs when the realistic avoidance reaction produces a sense of shame or humiliation and begins to involve psychic defensive reactions as well as physiological ones. For example, avoidance of white-hot objects is not considered a phobia. It is an elementary protective reaction. Similarly, the avoidance of deep water when one is a poor swimmer and has recently had to be rescued from drowning would not be called a water phobia. However, if such an experience should produce a total avoidance of bathing and spread to other symbolic situations in which breathing may be interfered with, it might then become a phobia and not a simple avoidance reaction.

There is some inclination to attempt to make a distinction by implying that the simple avoidance reactions are based on conscious factors while the phobia is involved with unconscious elements; however, this is neither satisfactory nor correct. Phobias may originate and persist in the face of clear knowledge of the factors involved. An elevator phobia is not the result of the possibility of physical danger involved in a falling elevator but is related to the necessity of being able immediately to get clear of other people when one becomes anxious. The anticipation of panic is related to the need to move swiftly when anxiety supervenes and even the seconds or fraction of a second in going from one floor to the next is too long. In addition, there is the apprehension that the elevator might get stuck and not open at all. This reaction is reminiscent of the nightmare in which one is unable to move and to be in control of one's activities at all times.

In all such phobias the element of danger is not the issue. The panic and humiliation which might ensue if the person does go out of control is the basic content of the phobic avoidance; thus the relationship to the phobic object is symbolic rather than literal and it represents a more generalized psychic danger rather than a specific physical danger.

Phobias often appear quietly and without any precipitating event. They also occur under circumstances in which the relationship of anxiety in connection with the phobic object may not be evident. It is easy to understand the avoidance of airplanes after a dangerous or unpleasant flight. The avoidance of elevators, open spaces, or other varieties of phobias is often difficult to understand. The phobia cannot be comprehended on rational grounds, even though rational explanations might be made for its existence. In addition, the phobia may not specifically involve a particular element in the situation but may generalize to include a total event or class of things. Phobias may involve single elements, such as flowers, or brown elevators with a capacity of six occupants. Generally, however, the phobia involves broader categories—such as open spaces which include flowers, trees, streets, or buildings. In addition, the phobia tends to involve similar objects or situations which have emotional factors in common. A phobia of elevators, for example, may also include phobias of narrow spaces, or mechanical objects which are not connected to the outside or other noticeable escape routes.

The phobia involves an idea or a content of experience rather than the object itself. The phobic object has symbolic significance; it is this that distinguishes it most clearly from simple avoidance reactions.

Unlike phobias, avoidance reactions have a high rate of cure. Simple avoidance reactions can be influenced with comparative ease by drugs, reconditioning, or hypnotic techniques. Phobias, on the other hand, are extremely difficult to influence, even with extensive therapy. The additional dimension of psychic involvement (over and above the somatic response) complicates the therapy most emphatically. It is this difference which accounts for the discrepant claims for some therapeutic approaches with regard to curing phobias. Exaggerated claims of cures are based on the failure to distinguish between true phobias and simple avoidance reactions.

In addition to the difficulty of distinguishing between the simple avoidance reaction and the phobia, there is a tendency to use the terms fear, phobia, and anxiety as synonyms. While they are clearly related and can coexist side by side, they are not identical. Fear is defined by Webster as "a painful emotion marked by alarm, awe, or anticipation of danger." It is not synonymous with phobia, which is defined as "an irrational or persistent fear of a particular object or objects." Fear can be present with or without a phobia; a phobia invariably contains an element of fear. In spite of the fact that in his psychiatric dictionary Hinsie defines 211 phobias in terms of fear only, fear is not a phobia. Hinsie's definitions range from fear of air, animals, and anything new, to fear of weakness, wind, women, work, and writing. This elaborate list attests only to early ignorance of the subject and the presumption that each item represented a different disorder; it simply identifies the phobic object without clarifying its significance in the dynamics of phobias.

The distinction between fear and anxiety is difficult to make and presently there is no consensus about the distinction. Freud made it in terms of conscious and unconscious derivatives. Others, such as Kurt Goldstein and Harry Stack Sullivan, see the difference as qualitative and consider that anxiety is experienced when the psychological integrity of the organism is at stake, while fear is experienced when the physiological integrity of the organism is at stake. This distinction applies to the difference between the simple avoidance reactions, in which the threat is physiological, and the phobias, wherein the threat is psychological.

ANXIETY AND OTHER FACTORS

Anxiety is described as a warning signal, or a feeling of apprehension in response to some danger—often of an unknown source. While anxiety is an invariable accompaniment of the phobic states, a successful phobia can often disguise its presence. Like fear, anxiety is not synonymous with phobia; it can be manifested in many ways other than by phobia. On the other hand, anything can become a phobic object—and the particular object does not give any clues about the source of the anxiety. For example, a phobic state may develop around public appearances or about performing before audiences ("stage fright"). The issue need not be a particular place or event, or a specific fear or anxiety, but rather the broad spectrum of feeling under scrutiny by a critical or unfriendly audience. This response could take place not only in a theatre but also at parties or luncheons with one or two people. The apprehension is not that of a physical danger, but of being humiliated or laughed at, of making a fool of oneself by inadequate or uncontrolled behavior. It is the individual's pride system which is at stake, not his physical well-being.

A phobia develops when a person utilizing the obsessive-compulsive defense is faced with a situation in which he feels he cannot maintain control. If there has been a similar threat of possible loss of control on a previous occasion, then a guaranteed way of dealing with this possibility is to avoid such situations permanently. The phobic state achieves this avoidance, since mere anticipation or fantasy of the situation will produce sufficient anxiety to ward off any participation in it. Consequently, it is a most potent technique for control; indeed, it is infallible. One need never encounter a particular difficulty if there is a permanent injunction against ever facing it.

THE SPREAD OF PHOBIAS

Phobias have a characteristic tendency to spread. A phobia which involves large groups may gradually extend to smaller and smaller groups, so that ultimately the person can function only when he is alone. The spread is along symbolic lines as well as in terms of the superficial content of the phobia. Such a spread has been explained by the conditioned reflex theorists as "stimulus generalization," or conditioning at a higher level of integregation. However, the tendency for the phobia to spread can be better understood on the grounds that similar psychic dangers in various situations may be included in the total phobia. Insisting on an aisle seat or one next to a door in a theatre or in other large halls is a partial solution to the fear of enclosure or lack of quick exit. The anxiety of being kept in an elevator even for seconds, or being unable to get through a crowd immediately, involves an inability to take the consequences of ordinary living—where one cannot always do immediately what one wishes. The phobic person demands immediate and absolute relief, whether it be in the form of a tranquillizer or a rapid, evasive action. Like those of an over-indulged child, his needs must be fulfilled at once. The phobia is a way of making certain of this fulfillment; through the phobia, life becomes organized in such a way as to guarantee that one will not be uncomfortable, even for the briefest moment.

Once a phobia begins, continued public exposure causes it to spread. One young woman developed a writing phobia which began in a bank. Soon she was unable to sign her name in a department store, then in a restaurant, and she finally reached the point where having to hold a cup or anything would cause hand tremors and uneasiness. While the spread of her phobia reduced the chances of exposing her lack of control, it also limited her dealings with others, so that she could eat only in the presence of her immediate family.

Phobias can develop around an infinite variety of situations or objects. The limitless possibilities of anything's becoming a phobic object has produced an extremely large list of phobias—from generalized ones such as school phobias to discrete ones such as phobias about blue horses or four leaf clovers. The term *school phobia*, for example, generally implies a fear of or resistence to going to school. It gives us no clue as to whether the phobic object is the school bus, the driver, the teacher, the desk, other pupils, or the brown dog who prowls about the school. For a clearer understanding of the phobic process it is important to recognize that in speaking of a school phobia one is not describing a specific condition but a generalized situation in which a specific factor operates. In order to treat such situations it is necessary to determine the precise factors which produce the phobic response. These factors are invariably symbolic representations of some aspect of the broader situation.

In the years prior to a dynamic understanding of the phobic process it was believed that each phobia had a separate etiology and dynamic function. Freud adopted this view of the phobic state even though he felt that the phobic object always symbolized some sexual fear. More recently the theory of phobias has assumed a less specific etiology.

If a person has a great fear of his hostile or aggressive feelings it is not surprising that any phobia he might develop would involve dangerous weapons or access to the hated person if he felt that under some circumstances he might lose control of himself. In the same way a person who fears exposure of his weaknesses or imperfections or his inability to exert absolute control may develop phobias about situations in which these deficiencies might be exposed. Thus the significance of a phobia may be the same even if the phobic objects are different. Some theorists have pointed out that the phobic object may be related to inner conflict; however, it may also have nothing to do with such a problem.

The phobia, however, does begin in the sensory context of a critical attack of anxiety and the symbolic associations may or may not be made with the original unconscious sources of fear. The phobic object, however, is distinctly related to the sensory context of the critical anxiety situation and does not, in itself, constitute the symbolism or the significance of the underlying fear. All phobias have the same dynamic and functional significance. The phobic object or situation is an accidental or coincidental accompaniment of a severe state of anxiety, when the person has experienced the possibility of going out of control. The content of the phobia is then woven around the situation when the anxiety occurred. The fact that certain situations are conducive to setting off severe anxieties about loss of control—such as heights, elevators, closed spaces, or dangerous weapons—accounts for the high incidence of such objects in the phobic states. Certain situations, such as stage appearances or social settings, may be the frequent objects of phobias as in these circumstances severe anxieties about being out of control may also arise.

In therapy the phobic object is of a secondary role. What must be analyzed and clarified is the fear of losing control which first manifested itself in an atmosphere in which, for some reason, the person experienced a panic or some severe anxiety. The analysis of the basic character structure in which this problem forms the hard core: *it is the obsessive-compulsive character structure.*

The dynamics of the phobic state are illustrated in an obsessional individual who had an intense fear of losing control and of being uncertain what might happen should he faint on a strange street. He began to avoid the streets of large cities, and soon the streets of smaller cities as well. Finally his phobia extended to the streets of his own city. This patient's phobia began when he was in his early twenties and was attending college in a mid-Western town. One evening, while on his way home from a movie, he was picked up by a police cordon in an area where a burglary had been committed. Since he had some difficulty proving that he had been in the movie at the time the crime was committed, he was held in custody for several hours. Afterwards he was fearful whenever he was on the streets alone; he felt powerless to protect himself. His apprehension became an overpowering obsession and whenever he was out alone he would need a witness to make him more comfortable. For a time these phobic fears diminished. Following a short-lived romance with a young woman at a summer resort his phobic fears became severe enough to require treatment.

His behavior at the time was indicative of his character structure, which made his phobias comprehensible. He met the young lady on the night of his arrival at the resort. She seemed to like him, and he became very enthusiastic about his conquest, fantasizing a major romance and possible marriage. She seemed to reciprocate most of his feelings, but suggested moving a bit more cautiously. When she seemed to be too friendly toward other guests, he became irritated and infuriated, and began to feel abused and taken advantage of. One evening he decided that he was through paying her bar bill while she flirted with other men. Although he said nothing to her about this, he sulked, acted hurt, and lost all his previous animation and enthusiasm. She wondered what was happening, but he could not tell her what he really felt because it seemed extreme even to him.

On the following day she was quickly put off by his hurt accusing attitude, and began avoiding him. This served to justify his suspicions, but as she withdrew, he made some tentative attempts to win her back. However, he was already too angry, too certain that she was a tease, and too annoyed when she did not apologize for her behavior of the previous evening. During the next few days she avoided him and he became morose and jealous as he watched her enthusiastic and joyful encounters with others. He finally cut his vacation short.

He was extremely upset over this event and his phobia returned with increased strength. It was at this point that he came for therapy. Exploration of his behavior at the summer resort clearly showed that he was imperious, grandiose, and egocentric.

He could not share the girl with her friends nor could he tolerate her friendly behavior toward others. In spite of their short acquaintance he demanded that she should devote herself exclusively to him since he had committed himself to her. He tried to control and direct her behavior according to his program and his needs. He could not make the demand openly, however, and when she behaved in a friendly fashion toward others, he felt rejected—although she obviously liked him and was as friendly toward him as she was toward her other acquaintances. It was this aspect of her personality which had attracted him to her in the first place, though it also made him anxious. His perfectionistic demands required that a woman be charming and attractive, with many friends and admirers, yet focus her attention exclusively upon him. While he might have clarified the situation by telling her how he felt, he would also have revealed his weakness—which was loneliness and fear of competition. He hoped to convey his demands by hurt looks and a sulking, scolding attitude, as though through some magical mind reading or thought transference she would know what produced his distress. His withdrawal changed the hitherto pleasant relationship into a tense and uneasy one that was hardly worth her pursuing. Her behavior then served to confirm his distortions and proved what he inevitably expected, and what his actions generally caused to happen.

The whole incident was a clear example of his insistent need to maintain control over his relationships so that they would proceed according to his plans. He could not take chances; he had to know, even before it was possible, that he was in complete control. This kind of person expects an absolute commitment from others in order to feel certain of their loyalty.

His phobia made no sense to him whatsoever, particularly since it was reactivated following his summer holiday. His ambivalent feelings toward his mother as well as his aggressive attitudes were explored in relation to his phobias. The problem of guilt and the fear of exposure of his unconscious needs to steal were also explored with regard to the initial experience at age twenty. While these issues had some relevance, the consistent element in the early experience as well as in his later experiences was the factor of fear of losing control. At 20 it was the fear of being out of control on the streets, unable to defend himself and without friends to support him should he faint or become ill. Moreover, it would be humiliating and intolerable to convey to others that he felt anxious on the streets or in crowds. He recognized that in the presence of people whom he had no need to impress or those with whom he felt in complete control, he felt no anxieties when confronted with such situations. But in the presence of others the condition was aggravated—especially when he wanted these others to acknowledge his strength and worldliness. All his phobias were direct representations of his overwhelming concern with fainting and losing control, about which he envisaged the most humiliating and dangerous consequences. In his sex life the lack of control manifested itself in his inability, most of the time, to delay orgasm longer than a few seconds, and he would frequently ejaculate prior to entrance. This was also a great source of distress to him and had begun to produce phobic avoidance of intercourse in order to prevent this failure. The vicious circle—refraining from intercourse to avoid exposing his prematurity—leads to such infrequent sexual contacts that when intercourse does take place the excitement is too great to permit control of the orgasm, further aggravating the anxiety which stimulates the production of the phobia. Because of his increasing concern about the premature ejaculation and impotence he began to have fantasies of intercourse with young girls, with whom he would feel entirely in control. At times these fantasies became very pressing and frightening, and yet were the only means by which he could visualize successful, prolonged intercourse. His so-called perverted interests were directly related to his difficulties in controlling his living in both sexual and nonsexual matters. He was therefore attracted to situations and people where his power to control was clear and manifest. This is frequently the basis on which an adult contemplates activities with young children, sexual or otherwise. In this way the adult can feel superior, better informed, and clearly the master of the situation. In sexual terms this is undeniably true, since children usually have either no knowledge of sexual matters or so little that they are less informed and experienced than an adult. Thus there is no possibility of humiliation, criticism, or of feeling inferior to the child—even though such a relationship may be most vicious and destructive.

CLINICAL TYPES AND THE OBSESSIONAL STATE

Phobias occur in obsessional characters—either as part of an obsessive-compulsive neurosis or as the prominent symptom when the obsessional way of life is secondary. The presence of a phobia indicates that the obsessional mechanism is not serving its purposes; and the phobic state intervenes to guarantee avoidance and absolute control in threatened areas of the personality structure. There are four clinical possibilities in the relationship of obsessional states to phobias:
1. Obsessional state without phobias;
2. Obsessional state with mild phobic symptoms;
3. Obsessional state with moderate phobic symptoms; and
4. Obsessional state with severe phobic symptoms.

Without Phobic Symptoms

In this state one finds the classical situation of an obsessional disorder, which may be characterized by manifestations of doubting, indecision, or compulsive acts. There are no phobic avoidance symptoms that are crystallized out of the matrix of the generally distracting and avoiding tendency of the obsessional mechanism. While there is considerable anxiety about engaging in any activity or initiating any project, there is no specific bar or obstacle aside from a generalized unwillingness to commit oneself. The reluctance to make decisions or to select alternatives often presents the picture of a person avoiding involvements, but these avoidance reactions are not yet sufficiently organized to constitute phobias.

Under such circumstances the obsessional patterns are sufficiently potent and successful in warding off severe anxiety attacks without the necessity of imposing absolute safeguards, as in the phobias. This does not mean that the person is healthier, or even that he functions more efficiently. It does imply that the obsessional technique is capable of exerting enough control to make other techniques unnecessary. This may mean that the person is actually less effective, i.e., it may be *more efficient* to isolate one area of living and close it off to further experiencing and to allow the rest of the person's living to go relatively untouched rather than to be subject to the generally inhibiting and depressive effect of obsessional doubting and indecisiveness and to minimize all involvements.

With Mild Phobic Symptoms

In this state we find the obsessive-compulsive neuroses with one or more phobic problems, all secondary to the main issues. The phobias frequently relate to the content of the obsessions or the compulsions. For example, the obsessional preoccupation may involve murder, and the individual may have a marked phobia regarding knives and guns. In most instances the phobias involve the issue of losing control in particular areas in which the person may have had an experience that endangered his control.

Generally the phobias do not occupy the central role in the therapy and often may go unnoticed as part of the patient's problem. Therapy centers on the obsessive-compulsive problem and the phobia frequently disappears without any focus being directed to it.

With Moderate Phobic Symptoms

In this group the phobic manifestations of the person's difficulties often predominate and the emphasis of therapy tends to be on the phobic problems rather than on the underlying obsessional state. More often than not the phobias force the person into therapy; he may be unaware of his obsessional problems. Such patients are often categorized as phobic and they prove quite resistant to hypnosis, conditioning, or other therapies designed exclusively to alter the phobic manifestations. It is these cases that illustrate the very close relationship of phobias to the obsessional state.

Such was demonstrated in a patient who came to therapy for what was described as an occupational phobia. While working, he experienced a sudden, rapid rise in pulse, accompanied by fear of fainting; he was forced to terminate the conference he was engaged in. After this incident he avoided all conferences. In the precipitating episode, the patient thought he was having a heart attack and subsequently was obsessionally preoccupied with his cardiac state for many years. In addition to this phobia, he also had phobias about bridges, enclosed spaces, and tunnels of all sorts. As time went on he developed a speaking phobia whenever he was called upon to give a prepared address. When called upon unexpectedly, he could function very well, and could speak quite persuasively.

Prior to the fainting spell he had experienced other difficulties in his job, since he always had to do it perfectly. He would prepare his work with exceptional thoroughness. This tendency annoyed some people at work, who considered it unnecessary and excessive. His life was organized around being a dedicated man of integrity who was beyond reproach in both his private and professional life. He took on total responsibility for the fate of his clients and their problems, and had great difficulty distinguishing between doing the best he could for them and filling *all* their needs. Many people thought highly of him, since his successes outweighed his defeats by far. He spent an inordinate amount of time trying to satisfy his need always to be certain and correct.

The fainting spell occurred when a colleague introduced an argument which he had not anticipated; he was taken unaware. He immediately became very tense, excited, and extremely restless. His pulse became very rapid and he felt a sudden pain in his chest. It is relevant that the unexpected argument was neither significant nor crucial. However, because it was unexpected, it could not be dealt with in the ideal and perfect fashion.

Characteristically, his phobias were those of control. Since he could never achieve absolute certainty, clarity, and wisdom in every situation, his phobias avoided the challenge and the discovery of his human frailties. At the same time he felt weak and cowardly for avoiding them. He could dissipate these feelings by fantasizing that, but for the phobias, he could achieve the hero role and perform perfectly. This patient's problems arose directly out of his obsessional difficulties. As the obsessional problems were gradually clarified, many of the phobias were entirely resolved, while others showed marked improvement.

The second example is that of a 45-year-old man whose major problem—like that of the woman described earlier in the chapter—was a writing phobia which had its beginnings when he had to sign his name to a contract in the presence of other people. On that occasion he was in the spotlight and began to get uneasy about the possibility of losing his composure and shaking visibly. This would have been humiliating for him. By pleading illness he avoided the actual trial, but thereafter he could not sign his name at banks, department stores, or even at home in the presence of friends or strangers. His pride prevented him from informing anyone except his wife. The major focus in this phobia was the issue of displaying a tremor which would betray his nervousness. The writing phobia gradually extended to a phobia about socializing wherever drinks were to be served, including luncheons, cocktails, and dinners. His social life became restricted because of the agitation produced in anticipation of such engagements. The phobias served a vital purpose for him, and at the same time were unacceptable to him. He felt ashamed and disappointed in himself for not being able to overcome these weaknesses. He was a very bright person who could not tolerate any situation in which he was second best or less well-informed than anyone else. Socializing was difficult for him apart from the tremors, as he could never know in advance whether he could measure up to all the people he might encounter. He was afraid that if he did not know everything, others would find him dull. His emphasis was entirely on intellectual achievement and although he recognized the impossibility of competing with everyone about everything, he actually expected always to be the best. Anything less than this was unacceptable to him, because to be less than perfect meant to be humiliatingly ordinary. Although he wanted his phobias eliminated he did not want to alter his perfectionistic goals and his requirement of omniscience. The phobias directly intervened at times when he felt endangered or was in danger of appearing human and therefore limited and imperfect. His obsessional problems were manifest in his demands for perfection, control, guarantees of the future, and in specific matters such as his meticulous concern for his own person and affairs and his obsessional rumination, preoccupations, and rituals.

With Severe Phobic Symptoms

In this category one finds the phobic condition so much in the foreground that the underlying obsessive-compulsive patterns are frequently either in the background or completely hidden. It is under these circumstances that one is led to a separate category called "phobic states"—the phobias appear to be the sole problem which requires treatment. The content of the phobias may be varied and diffuse and, at times, may not give any clues to the underlying obsessive-compulsive state which is invariably present.

For example, a particularly severe phobia about animals prevented a very prosperous businessman from entering any house or establishment until he was assured that there were no animals on the premises. This phobia was closely related to a dirt phobia which necessitated his washing his hands dozens of times during the day and changing his clothes three or four times a day. The phobic issues were so incapacitating that the compulsive handwashing ritual was considered secondary and unimportant. These phobias alternated with other strong phobic reactions to particular places and things, but essentially the problem centered about the issue of germs, dirt, and other noxious elements.

This man was an extremely successful entrepreneur who managed very large financial deals. He sought help only from banks. He felt he could trust no one as others would inevitably let him down. He was a "lone operator" who was convinced of his invincible capacity—and afraid that at any moment he might not be able to meet his financial obligations and thus lose everything. He was in a constant state of tension, preoccupied with ways of guaranteeing his next payments and making certain of his future. He could enjoy neither his money nor his possessions because of his constant concern as to whether any of it would be there tomorrow. Every restaurant bill, charity drive, or legitimate demand was scrutinized with great care to guard against his being victimized. Objectively his financial situation was most secure, but he directed all his efforts to making certain that tomorrow would be exactly like today. He had no interest in the tendencies he displayed towards omnipotence or omniscience, and saw the whole difficulty as a peculiarity of his phobias, which he wanted to eliminate.

The phobic problem was certainly central both in his thoughts and in the limitations in his living, while the obsessional difficulties were in the background. The phobias expressed his insistence on a purity and perfection that was impossible to achieve. His extensive handwashing was designed to guarantee his health. The animal phobia was a concern focused on preventing the passage of organisms from animal hosts. Any contact, even the most remote, would require washing and a change of clothes. This is an extreme form of control in attempting to dictate to the world what contacts it should make with him and what it should keep out of his range. It was often evident that the germ phobia was a device to distract him from his greater concern, namely, the need to have a guaranteed financial structure to demonstrate to the world—and particularly to his father—that he was invincible and unassailable. To fail meant that he would be totally rejected by all and expelled from the human race as inadequate and imperfect.

The phobia is thus an excellent technique of defense against anxiety. The anxiety is clearly related to personality character-istics which are in danger of being exposed or destroyed. They may involve covert hostilities, fear of being weak and dependent, or may cover the entire range of human conflict. The underlying character structure which is organized to maintain a rigid control against exposure of acknowledgement is the obsessive-compulsive dynamism which is ideally set up to serve this purpose. Under circumstances in which the obsessive-compulsive dynamism is not sufficiently intact, the phobia, with its absolute avoidance, guar-antees against exposure by never permitting the situation to develop. Consequently, the phobia becomes a technique for absolute control, and unless it becomes too diffuse or widespread it serves its purpose well. It is, however, qualitatively different from the simple avoidance reactions that serve the same purpose of protecting the person from known sources of danger. The phobia arises in response to a severe and critical anxiety attack in which some psychological need, defense, or conflict is brought dangerously near to being exposed or of going out of control.

The setting or sensory accompaniments determine the phobic object in which the real danger may or may not be symbolically represented. The phobic object may be entirely accidental or coincidental, and may involve the sensoria in auditory, kinesthetic, or visual senses. The symbolism and setting frequently combine and the spread of the phobia is determined both by sensory con-tiguity and by the symbolic associations possible in the new set-ting. The phobia is, in essence, an avoidance technique established through the defensive capacities of the human psyche to prevent the destruction of the integrity of the organism. However, it is the neurotic integration and, consequently, the necessity for symbolism and other devices to represent both unconscious and out-of-awareness needs and conflicts that is essential.

Recognition of the origin of the phobia from an obsessive-compulsive disorder makes it clear that the ultimate resolution of the phobia rests upon clarifying the obsessive-compulsive dif-ficulty.

CHAPTER 7

Breakdown of
the Obsessive
Defense

T he obsessive defense pattern is excellently
suited to providing someone with a feeling
of security in a world in which uncertainty is inevitable. However, critical situations—which may be caused by disease, social
upheavals, catastrophic events, or accidental circumstances—may
be sufficiently severe so that the obsessional integration can no
longer be maintained. Crises such as these may be the result of
wars, the death of significant people in one's life, or physical
changes in the course of one's development. Such changes are
common in the aging process; they are particularly significant
during adolescence, when marked psychological and physiological demands are made on the individual. The maturation of
the gonads during this period produces physiological tensions
which are entirely beyond one's control, and usually push the
person toward sexual intimacy. At the same time, social and
cultural pressures may require the youth to become independent

and make vocational decisions, as well as achieving some hetero-
sexual intimacy of a sexual and nonsexual nature. Some of these
pressures may be controlled and limited by the individual while
others are sufficiently powerful to demand conformity. Adolescence, therefore, is an era of great turmoil and decision; any obsessional patterns which have been successful until then may
break down. One begins to feel weak, powerless, and incapable
of handling all the demands. It is no surprise that the adolescent
era has such a high percentage of schizophrenic episodes.

If lustful needs are very great, and the person's skill in making contact with the opposite sex is not adequate, the youth may
experience a good deal of difficulty unless he can control such
needs. Obsessional defenses are most commonly utilized to
control these desires and to keep the person's anxieties to a
minimum. His ability to do so will depend upon his own capacities and on the availability and quality of sex partners. Therefore
we may find that in some adolescents a minor event may produce a major breakdown, while in other individuals the most
traumatic events seem to be handled with considerable ease. The
capacity is directly related to the experience and self-esteem
which has been established prior to adolescence. The success of
obsessional patterns will depend upon the extent to which they
have been needed to support the security structure prior to adolescence—so that the increased strain will not cause the structure
to collapse. Harry Stack Sullivan developed this point of view
most effectively and demonstrated how the breakdown of obsessional defenses may result in a schizophrenic disintegration of
the personality structure.

The variety of psychological defenses which a person utilizes
in order to deal with anxiety will rarely dissipate the anxiety
entirely. A neurosis is essentially a collection of such defenses
constituting a personality structure which attempts to minimize
and deflect the anxiety. The success of these defensive tactics
depends upon the severity of the realistic issues which the individual must meet and the strength of his resources outside the
neurotic tendency. The obsessional defense, when functioning

efficiently, is capable of handling large amounts of anxiety unless it dislocates the person's life or alienates him from others to the extent that it may stimulate even more anxiety.

The obsessional's desire to overcome his feelings of powerlessness by a firm determination to know everything and to guarantee his future existence cannot really succeed because the neurosis can provide only an illusory solution. His failure to achieve omniscience—which would eliminate anxiety—must be defended either by denial or by a variety of devices which serve to minimize his awareness of this deficiency. The phobia is often the technique used to maintain an illusion of perfection by avoiding the areas that would expose these deficiencies. It allows one to maintain an illusion of omnipotence on the assumption that one could manage everything if only one were rid of the phobia.

Ordinarily, an individual attempts to minimize his anxiety through judicious planning or by restraining his demands and expectations, thereby avoiding the need to test his resources. The obsessional also tries to avoid challenges. However, this is not always possible and such challenges may produce an outbreak of the existing obsessional patterns or initiate new ones. The presence of an obsessional technique demands a greater display of one's omnipotence which, in turn, forces the person to recognize his limitations—thereby stimulating more obsessional tactics. This produces the typical neurotic circle in which the presence of anxiety stirs up defenses which produce more anxiety.

This vicious circle can be interrupted if one is willing to accept being human—which means to be prepared to accept uncertainty. As long as one insists on absolute control, he will be unable to disrupt the obsessional way of life because the world continues to be potentially destructive. The obsessional device is more comforting to him and appears more reasonable than a recognition of his human limitations. *It is this seemingly obvious choice which makes the obsessive pattern so adhesive, and explains why the obsessive clings to his defenses with such tenacity —even while he recognizes their paradoxical value.*

When the obsessional defenses are no longer capable of dealing with the demands on the inside or outside of the person, several possible developments may ensue. It has already been demonstrated that a depression may follow a failure to sustain the obsessional's illusions of his capacities. Under other circumstances there could be an increase in one's activities, with agitated efforts to overcome the demands and avert a breakdown. The agitated behavior may be associated with an increase and extension of the obsessional patterns; if unrestrained, this development could produce a panic. Should a panic occur and continue unchecked, schizophrenic disintegration of the personality structure may follow. Sullivan emphasized this sequence of events in the beginnings of schizophrenia. In his classical study of schizophrenia, Bleuler noted that compulsive ideas occur regularly in schizophrenia and manifest themselves early in the illness. It is notable that in adolescence the obsessional illnesses frequently precede the development of schizophrenia.

Some recent theorists have hypothesized that obsessional defenses are an attempt to prevent a schizophrenic disintegration of the ego. This notion implies that a neurosis is an attempt to immunize an individual against a possible psychotic breakdown. This view has less support, however, than the concept that mental illness is a part of a broader spectrum extending from normal to psychotic—with the neurotic development somewhere near the middle. It emphasizes the more prevalent notion that these disorders are different from the normal only quantitatively, not qualitatively; they are simply exaggerations of tendencies prevalent in all people.

TYPES OF DEFENSES

In the spectrum of mental illness the type of defense constitutes the symptoms of the neurosis or psychosis. One could hypothesize that certain defenses are related to certain mental illness or that one type of defence may be exclusively present in a particular nosological category. This notion has been expressed by many psychiatrists and psychoanalysts, but I believe it is not a valid theoretical assumption. It would be incorrect to say that the obsessional type of defense implies a greater degree of personality disorganization than does the hysterical defense simply because it utilizes more extreme techniques. Exactly the opposite situation may be true. Yet this notion has sometimes led to a snobbish glorification of the obsessional schizophrenic defense.

It was thought that the introspective, highly sensitized obsessional had greater capacities for self-understanding, as well as for understanding others. This attitude led some researchers to assume that the schizophrenic had particular talent for interpreting dreams and other symbolic or unconscious productions. The extravagant, dramatic, hysteric was viewed as being overly concerned with the outer world in contrast to the obsessional, who was more preoccupied with his inner world.

The type of defense and the symptoms which are developed in a particular neurosis or psychosis are closely related to the problems the person has to deal with in his life. It may be a matter of utilizing the same defenses which he observes in his parents, or developing suitable defenses to deal with his parents' personality traits. For example, if the situation is extremely threatening, the technique of denial or dissociation may be utilized to allow for simple survival. On the other hand, the obsessional parent who makes demands upon his children for absolute performances and perfect achievements will be fostering obsessional patterns in the children, who will have to cope with these demands.

Some defenses involve the utilization of physiological mechanisms or somatic sources for influencing or shaping the environment. Some defenses allow the organism to function more effectively temporarily by focusing away from painful or significant issues. Among other devices, sublimation, suppression, repression, denial, and selective inattention function in this way. In general, most personality types use all three modalities of defense organization even though one may be more prominent and more influential in controlling the person's behavior.

By reducing anxiety such defenses may accelerate learning to a certain extent, but in the long run they tend to interfere with the learning process. The defense which enables a person to appear to others the opposite of what he really feels is called a reaction formation. A highly competitive person may appear to himself and to others to be a most cooperative individual, entirely disinterested in competitive struggles. This defense enables him to function in situations in which some cooperation is necessary, but it interferes with the process and inevitably disrupts it because the competitive strivings manifest themselves in covert and accidental ways when the person cannot identify his true interests; he cannot confront them or deal with them and they subtly defeat his goals in the long run. Reaction formations are generally not used for major personality constituents. If the issues are more significant and more drastic consequences could result from an awareness of such needs or tendencies, more rigorous defenses may be needed. Denial is such a defense.

Denial

In denial a person does not recognize a personality trait which is unacceptable to him, even though it is obvious to others and is brought to his attention. The obsessional substitutions utilizing magic and rituals are a part of defenses which foster illusions of power and strength by denying the realities of existence up to a point. When the realities are completely denied and the person takes up an entirely new, unreal existence, he is manifesting a psychosis. This may occur when a previously denied or dissociated feeling or impulse is brought forcibly to a person's awareness. His inability to accept it may produce panic and a disintegration of his personality structure.

In the psychotic defense, when one takes on a new identity, one strives to document his new self by a denial of the facts relative to his old self. While adducing proofs regarding his new identity, he may deny his family, friends, and backgrounds and not even acknowledge that he is in a mental hospital. The new identity may be tenaciously supported in spite of extensive intellectual assaults and the absence of any confirmation from the environment. Such delusions are quite common in psychotic states.

However, the type of defense employed does not determine the presence or absence of mental illness—even though defenses can be graded according to their closeness or distance from reality. We may find evidence of obsessional substitution, denial, and fantasies bordering on delusions in people who are functioning quite effectively while the psychotic patient who is severely withdrawn may be rationalizing in a way reminiscent of healthy, unneurotic living. It is not the type of defense employed, but the extremes to which that defense is used. All the defenses are used by most people—ranging from the normal to the psychotic. Some defenses may be more prominent than others because they are more extensively utilized and become the dominant personality traits. Diagnostic categories have often reflected these main defenses and have given a label to the disorders involved. Such a label does not mean, however, that what is named is the only defense that is being employed. The diagnosis of hysteria in a person need not mean that other defensive techniques are not also present. The obsessional device present in all personality types is called obsessional living or obsessional neurosis only when it dominates the personality picture. All categories of mental illness contain several defenses, with one predominating. One can identify the obsessional defenses in hysterias, anxiety states, psychosomatic disorders, and manic depressive and schizophrenic disorders. Whatever the diagnosis, however, its role is similar to what has already been described.

Some Mistaken Notions

While the severity of a mental illness is often closely related to the major defensive technique employed, there is no hierarchy of illness beginning with hysteria and progressing to schizophrenia. A hysterical illness may be completely disruptive and incapacitating, while an ambulatory or intermittent schizophrenic may be functioning at a rather high level of adjustment—perhaps higher than that of the hysteric. It is this mistaken notion that has produced the concern that the obsessional neurotic who is functioning adequately may regress into a nonfunctioning schizophrenic if he is improperly treated. Similarly, it has been suggested that the resolution of a schizophrenic disorder would regularly produce an obsessional disorder which, if maintained would immunize the person against schizophrenia. While such back-and-forth swings do occur, they do not occur because of their hierarchical relationship. Generally speaking, the obsessional pattern of living rarely disintegrates for the worse and only with the utmost skill and activity can it be altered for the better. Usually it is quite stable and is an effective development which may be disorganized only in the face of extreme circumstances. It is because the obsessional pattern has such stability that therapy is most difficult. The very nature of the defense, with its capacity for distraction, emotional isolation, denial, grandiosity, doubting, etc., makes it difficult to undermine the obsessional defense. Only when the patient can be made to feel that some benefit can be derived from any change can we hope to achieve it.

However, there is some validity to the idea that a neurosis may protect the individual against a psychotic breakdown since the longer one has managed to function effectively with a neurosis the less likely is a psychotic breakdown to occur in later years, when the demands on one's living have lessened. This is not always true, however, in the obsessional neurosis—when aging is accompanied by the actual lessening of one's physical and mental capacities, a fact which the obsessional cannot accept. The accompaniments of aging, with its diminution of psychological and physical capacities, can and do aggravate the obsessional disorder.

A predominantly obsessional illness can become, particularly in the later years, an involutional depression or a schizophrenic illness with delusions and hallucinations. Usually such people may have been functioning successfully until the crisis of aging overtook them. This would suggest that a neurosis does not necessarily ward off a psychosis. In addition, the tendency in younger people to move back and forth, from an obsessional neurosis to a withdrawn schizophrenic state, also negates the notion of the immunizing power of a neurosis.

Possible Regressions

Is there a particular kind of obsessional neurosis which tends to regress into schizophrenia? While there is little support for the notion that certain kinds of obsessions are more likely to precede schizophrenia, it has been noted by some that when somatic preoccupations are prominent or hypochondriasis is extreme there is a greater likelihood for schizophrenia to supervene. A shift in the patient's preoccupation with dirt or feces to his bowels and its activities can be the center around which psychotic delusions may develop. These delusions may involve the feeling of being poisoned, or of having no intestines because they were destroyed by some malevolent influence. A variety of delusions may focus around the feces. Or the obsessional's preoccupation with his heart and its functioning, and his uneasy vigilance lest the cardiac rate change, may be the prelude to a delusion concerning the heart. The intense anxiety surrounding this matter may actually alter the cardiac action, which may presage a psychosis.

In the transition from obsessionalism to schizophrenia, many features of these two syndromes can be noted and identified and it can be seen that they seem to serve the same purposes. The grandiosity of the obsessional is dealt with as a reality in the schizophrenic illness and the omniscient demands in the obsessional state become expressed as being God, or some other metaphoric superman. Phobic avoidance in the obsessional is manifested as total withdrawal and emotional isolation during the psychotic episode. The obsessional distractions of obfuscation and other complicated verbal operations can be recognized in the schizophrenic in his neologisms, autistic activity, and alienation of thought and feeling. The prevailing feeling of danger, threat, and anticipated humiliation and rejection is often translated as a paranoid system when a psychosis develops.

Often, the resulting psychosis appears to be an extreme extension of the previous obsessional symptoms. The individual can no longer manage, and what was previously odd but functional now appears to be "crazy" and totally unacceptable, maladaptive, and disruptive.

Under certain circumstances an extension of the obsessional patterns can lead to paranoid developments which, in turn, may become delusional and be part of a schizophrenic development. The uneasy, uncertain, obsessional person who scrutinizes every individual and event for evidence of criticism, contempt, or rejection sees every contact as a possible source of danger. He is set for attack and it is no wonder he often sees it coming. Since he must always be on top, correct and omniscient, every minor failure will be viewed with alarm and be accompanied by his feelings that the community will be pleased at his failure and will humiliate him. This is an ideal setting for the development of paranoid ideas—particularly when feelings of anger and hostility are also involved. The development of paranoid feelings which include expectations of malevolence from others inevitably follows the tendency to distort events and experiences so that one is always a victim. When one expectantly scrutinizes the behavior of others for evidences of reassurance, approval, or criticism, one does not take sufficient account of the possibility that the other person may be in some distress and may be focused on his own needs. This can mistakenly be interpreted as displeasure with or disapproval of the obsessional. Such a capacity for distortion arises from the obsessional's excessive need for approval and the assumption that everything that happens has relevance for him.

The obsessional person is unaware that he cannot always win the approval of others; thus any gesture from others, the significance of which is not clearly evident, is often viewed as expressing disapproval. He does not explore or inquire about this particular gesture—which may owe to indigestion or some other cause quite unrelated to him. The simple and regular explanation is that he is being criticized and disliked. This explanation also satisfies the obsessional's feeling of specialness and his expectation of being envied by others. He assumes the other person has reason to dislike him because he is so clever, capable, and successful, and that consequently the other person would like to knock him down and humiliate him. From this point of view of being special it is but a short step to the grandiosity of the psychotic, which is a regular part of the paranoid system.

Grandiosity—the ultimate effect of striving for omniscience, omnipotence, and the fulfillment of superhuman ideals—is an integral part of the obsessional disorder. While the obsessional proclaims his modesty and readiness to be satisfied with small achievements, his strivings and behavior belie this position. It is clear that he can be satisfied only with superhuman achievements. This is grandiosity in action—even though there is some embarrassment and denial when the obsessional is confronted with the full implication of such demands. The grandiosity of the paranoid state, on the other hand, is unashamedly expressed and aggressively defended—even though it consists of precisely those elements present in the obsessional state. Obsessional rituals and preoccupations are often indistinguishable from psychotic ritualistic performances, and they appear to serve the same purpose. While the obsessional ritual may be explained as silly and meaningless—*but necessary*, the schizophrenic makes no explanation for such behavior.

In spite of these similarities there is no direct continuum of obsessional neurosis into schizophrenia or vice versa, even though the schizophrenic may have an underlying obsessional personality structure. This situation was demonstrated in a young man whose life was filled with obsessive ritualistic practices involving Yoga-like exercises and hand-washing rituals as well as word games. He was immersed in "doing good" for all, while neglecting many essentials in his life. Periodically, however, under the stress of criticism at the job or difficulties with his wife or friends, he would express delusions of being God and plan to carry out some dangerous mission to prove this. The effect was only to produce damage to his professional standing. Instead of carrying out the dangerous missions, he would either admit himself or permit himself to be admitted to a mental hospital where, after a brief period of psychotherapy, he would temporarily abandon his delusions and return to the community. While such events might suggest an obsessional moving in and out of schizophrenia, the picture is essentially that of a psychotic individual who manages to keep his psychosis in control. This person demonstrates the close relationship of the obsessional defense with the schizophrenic illness, rather than the notion that one disorder regularly moves into the other.

Another example of the relationship between the obsessional personality structure and schizophrenia (and, particularly, the development of a paranoid delusion), is that of a young lady whose attempts to achieve God-like perfection occasionally took on messianic proportions in her soul-saving activities. She was enormously energetic and usually effective. Most of her activities were constructive up to the point where she would meet some opposition or criticisms. Then her activity would become more tense and frenetic, and her previously guarded behavior would be less restrained and become antagonizing and frightening to the community. She had some rituals, many compulsive patterns, and a great deal of preoccupation with being invulnerable, imperturbable, and invincible. On one occasion some mild restraints imposed on her behavior by others provoked a number of paranoid delusions in which she insisted that she was being followed by television cameras and was in danger of being killed. At this point she sought out therapy, and hospitalization was avoided. Her obsessive patterns began to unfold dramatically during therapy and this took the focus away from her paranoid tendencies. Her activities at home, socially, and at her job were severely obsessive, and her schizophrenic tendencies became manifest only during the therapy sessions. In general, she functioned quite effectively as a somewhat unusual woman who related to everyone in a sticky, obsessional fashion.

On one occasion during therapy, I had the opportunity to observe the development of a transient, paranoid delusion. The patient's capacity for introspection and the insight which she obtained from therapy allowed her to examine this incident in detail. One day, after finishing her teaching job, she noticed that a car seemed to be following her car. She concluded that the two men in the car were trying to force her to the side of the road and kill her. As she ruminated about this she began to panic and elaborate a detailed, paranoid delusion. She related this brief psychotic development several days later in her therapy hour. After this hour she wrote me a letter from which I quote. "I knew I hadn't pin-pointed the cause of discomfort during the hour with you. I kept at it as I returned home. The time I saw the two men pulling out in their car, as I got into mine, was in the afternoon. As I was closing up my desk I looked at a box full of pencils and ballpoint pens, etc.—probably 25 assorted ones or so. We're always running out of pencils at our house. I remember using one of the pens for record-taking, wanting to put it in my purse, and saying to myself: 'the discomfort you'll feel about this won't be worth the convenience of taking it.' It wasn't that I felt it would be missed, or that anyone would care . . . but that STEALING would register in my mind. As I was closing up, I rummaged through the box and took two pencils—middle size, somewhat beat up ones . . . put them in my purse. Now as I walked towards my car this came back, vividly, and I felt a sudden relief which made me feel this was the direct cause of the feeling 'they're going to get me' which occurred, timewise, not more than a half-hour later. As I thought of symbols, I burst out laughing, asking myself out loud, 'But why did you have to take TWO of them?' I hope you can help me answer that question—or rather, why did I *have* to take even one?"

As we explored the letter and all her feelings in connection with it, the following issues became clear: (1) she felt guilty about not behaving perfectly and not being in control of herself;

(2) she could not resist getting something for nothing; this was an integral part of her grandiosity; and (3) her perfectionism and self-righteousness could not allow her to take even one badly beat-up pencil and her rigid intolerance to any human frailty expected that her action would be followed by severe and immediate punishment.

When it was suggested that perhaps her taking the pencils did not merit such extreme consequences, her reply was: "Then you think it's all right to be a thief?" However, as our discussion proceeded she could relate the superhuman demands she made on herself with her expectations of retribution. At this understanding, her anxiety and paranoid feelings dissipated. She could relax and acknowledge that the initial repression of the incident and her ability to finally look at it removed the stored-up suspiciousness of others and her own feeling of phoniness, lack of integrity, and guilt which followed such a minor breach in her behavior. This incident enabled her to understand many of her previous delusional systems.

While the schizophrenic reaction does follow the breakdown of an obsessional defense, these changes are not necessarily stages in the same illness. The defensive structure evident in the psychosis can often be recognized in the obsessional dynamisms— but this is characteristic of all mental mechanisms which, in the extreme, participate in the psychoses. The obsessional neurosis, on the other hand, is closely related to schizophrenia, and the therapy of each can be enhanced through the understanding of both.

CHAPTER 8

Addictive States

Grandiosity is the assumption of an exalted, superior state which is beyond realistic possibility or actuality. While it is related to a feeling of high esteem and worth, it is qualitatively different. It is an illusory conception of strength, unjustified by actual or potential achievement. It is a defensive and adaptive development which arises out of certain psychological needs and is found regularly in psychopathological developments. Its characteristic presence in the obsessional neurosis casts some light on its adaptive role in the psychological problems of obesity, alcoholism, narcotic addiction, compulsive gambling, masturbation, and kleptomania. Grandiosity also plays a major role in nonaddictive disorders such as paranoia and psychopathic personality.

In all these conditions the common thread of grandiosity is to be found when the individual tends to assume a privileged status. In each instance the grandiose feelings are expressed in terms of being exempt from the consequences of one's behavior, and not being subject to the laws of nature, which accounts for the excesses in the person's activity.

It is a short step from a compulsive necessity to be universally capable, never deficient, and all-knowing to feeling superhuman.

DEVELOPMENT OF GRANDIOSITY

Omnipotent feelings have been described by many behavioral scientists as a usual accompaniment of certain periods of development, particularly infancy. Sigmund Freud, Sandor Ferenczi, Sandor Rado, and other personality theorists conceive of infancy as a period of unlimited power and influence during which the infant manages to get everything he wants with no limitations or restrictions. This has been called primal omnipotence, from which later feelings of grandiosity may develop. This assumption presupposes that the infant feels truly powerful and effective during the first year of his existence when his needs are automatically fulfilled or when his slightest effort is met with unlimited fulfillment. While it is true that under certain fortunate circumstances the infant may have a coterie composed of mother and "assistant mothers," as well as other significant adults who will cater immediately to his every need, the infant generally is in a most precarious position—dependent on the good will and attentive benevolence of the environment. What can be observed is that the infant is helpless and completely incapable of filling any of his own needs except for oxygen intake, provided he is suitably placed on his back. Otherwise he is entirely dependent upon others. It seems more reasonable, therefore, to speculate about the infant's feelings of *insecurity* rather than his feelings of omnipotence. One could emphasize the constant state of jeopardy he is in, and his readiness to fall into severe states of anxiety and panic. Rather than considering euphoria, one can find more evidence of potential panic, danger of asphyxiation, a potential for starvation, and the incapacity to communicate. The cry, which is often a most potent force in mobilizing attention to the infant's needs, can also produce the opposite effect when it is either misunderstood or when it falls on already distraught and anxious ears. Therefore, while the problems of omnipotence and grandiosity may have some roots in very early experiences, it is doubtful that there is a direct relationship. The experiences of early infancy and childhood may serve to enhance the adult's security and feeling of power and esteem if that stage was a successful period of development without too many thwarts or traumas. Such experiences could be reflected in the adult as comfortable feelings of self-worth, esteem, and respect. Grandiosity is the negation of real self-esteem; it denies one's real assets and demands impossible, superhuman attributes to overcome one's doubts.

The ability to influence the environment and to fulfill one's needs may develop valid feelings of esteem and power and may be the beginning of a stable and solid self-system. Difficulties during infancy rather than unlimited gratification may be the cause of the grandiosity that may develop in later life. Grandiosity may be the result of a thwarted and unsuccessful infancy during which one can manage to influence adults only with great difficulty, consequently always feeling himself to be on the edge of danger.

The feelings of uncertainty and threat because of neglect or malevolence require extreme measures to overcome. Omnipotent feelings may develop in order to establish certainties and to protect and guarantee one's existence. This is the early history of the future obsessional, whose need for control by an omnipotent, omniscient, ritualistic pattern of living emphasizes the uncertain, contradictory, and inconsistent relationships of those early years. Grandiosity and omnipotence are adaptive devices designed to deal with the apprehension of extreme threats. Such threats are most distressing during the periods of greatest dependency and realistic powerlessness, such as in infancy and childhood. As the person's actual powers and skills increase, his dependency may diminish—as may his need for special protective devices. If, however, his early patterns of dependency and insecurity are extreme, the development of his self-esteem may lag and he may remain helpless and dependent throughout his life.

There are some fortunate people whose early experiences leave them with a comfortable feeling of power and strength, derived from their ability to deal effectively with their needs. While they may be dependent in some matters, they can also satisfy their needs independently of others. Such people are confident and self-sufficient, but they are not grandiose. They are aware of their limitations and they are prepared to admit their deficiencies. Their goals and expectations are realistic. They do not swing from supreme confidence to profound self-derogation. Instead, they appear to have an ongoing, steady feeling of comfortable self-assurance which permits them to meet each new occasion with open curiosity rather than with dread and evasion. This state is called healthy self-assertion, or self-esteem, and it must be distinguished from grandiosity, which is a neurotic or psychotic defensive development. Healthy self-confidence, however maligned by the less fortunate, is a source of constructive energy, as opposed to the endless obsessional procrastinations and evasions (no matter how flamboyant the grandiosity).

ADDICTIVE DISORDERS

Grandiosity is a very notable element in the addictive disorders*—such as alcoholism, obesity, and drug addiction. While the issue of grandiosity does not constitute the entire problem,

---

* In an illuminating article on addiction, Henry A. Davidson notices the marked similarity of addiction to the compulsive neuroses. He was referring to the mounting tension in addicts—which seems to be relieved only by taking the addictive medication. He says: "Psychologically, it seems strikingly similar to a compulsive (neurotic) reaction. The kleptomaniac or pyromaniac will tell you, 'I get no pleasure out of stealing (or setting fires) but I have a mounting unendurable tension (or anxiety) which can be relieved in this way.'" Thus he points out that addiction is not an escape, but a search for a better life. (Davidson, H. A., Confessions of a Goof Ball Addict, Amer J Psychiat 120: 8, 1963.)

it plays a major role in the fantasy life of these individuals. The alcoholic and drug addict has a compulsive necessity to drink or take drugs and an incapacity to exert any reasonable control over his behavior in these areas. To this extent the condition is related to the obsessive-compulsive syndrome, wherein the issue of control is the essential feature. Once it is established, the addiction problem has a physiological basis as well as a psychological one. However, the underlying personality that lends itself to addictions is that of the obsessive-compulsive. The problem of control and the need to handle the anxieties that result from loss of control can be recognized as the overriding issue in people suffering from addictive disorders. While depression, anxiety, and a host of other psychological problems may be present, obsessional difficulties are omnipresent. The alcoholic, for example, is regularly described as a dependent person with a variety of obsessional symptoms, whose failure to control his impulses results in the excessive intake of alcohol. This enables him to overcome the recognition of his incapacity and to resort to the illusory power and fulfillment of his fantasy life. The same obsessional patterns which are successful in nonaddicts seem to fail periodically in addicts. They are forced to recognize their limitations and incapacities, which are ordinarily covered over by their obsessive technique. When this happens they may be sufficiently distressed to start drinking.

However, they may also begin an addictive debauch—whether it be drugs, food, or alcohol—when these techniques are successful. At such times, the person may become excited and overjoyed and react in the extreme to his achievement. This may develop into a euphoric grandiosity which allows him to indulge in his excesses and feel exempt from the consequences. Whether the anxiety is caused by failure or success, the addict is compulsively drawn to the object of his addiction. The recognition of an incomplete capacity to control oneself and the environment becomes an occasion for tossing over all controls and going to the opposite extreme—the binge. It is a commonplace that alcoholics cannot moderate their drinking. It is all or nothing. This is precisely the obsessional problem. After abandoning all controls and getting lost in alcoholic binges or drug reveries, the illusory superman can be revived in the grandiose fantasies of the intoxicated state. After an alcoholic bout there is great remorse and guilt, which produces the inevitable resolution to abandon the addiction. Since the underlying compulsion is untouched, the resolution has no chance of succeeding. The inability to honor his resolution only reinforces the awareness of his inability—which produces more drinking. The grandiose patterns that ensue not only serve temporarily to reinstate the illusion of superhuman capacity for control but also serve to deceive the person into believing that he *can* exert the necessary control whenever he decides to do so. This feeling of privilege and exemption from human frailties and natural laws plays a prominent role in the alcoholic addictive state. The alcoholic always insists that he can drink and that he can stop. This is simply a grandiose statement—with all the deception and illusion conveyed by such claims. The alcoholic may secretly believe his grandiose claims and his superior capacities and skills. He may even demonstrate it in his contempt for himself and others, before and during his alcoholic bout. He may admire his cleverness in deceiving others and feel he can outwit them in the never-ending hunt for the bottle. He is only emphasizing the grandiose view of himself and his exemption from being human. He cannot understand why others fail to believe or accept his superior status. The addiction or the compulsion to take alcohol or drugs, which ultimately produces a somatic or physiological craving after prolonged use, thus has its origins in a psychological deficit.

Rado described addiction in the following manner: "Addiction begins when use of a drug occurs at a time of acute distress from a serious physical illness or some point of chronic distress that may have been produced by a variety of causes (psychiatric disorder, physical incapacity, misfortune, etc.). The distressed and helpless patient craving for miraculous help has been sensitized to the pleasure effect of the narcotic drug. His intoxication (which he seeks to hide knowing that society condemns the misuse of narcotics) is the expression of his *exalted* feeling that with the help of the drug he has at long last brought about the longed-for change in his life." The drug deals with anxiety by erasing it, narcotizing it, and temporarily removing the realities of a distressing and intolerable situation. This is one of the most widespread techniques for dealing with anxiety in all cultures, through the ages. However, alcoholism and drug addiction, even though widespread, represent only a small proportion of those who take drugs or alcohol. The essential difference lies in the way an individual drinks and the way he controls it. Once the person gets beyond the possibility of choice and is forced to drink by pressures which he can neither control nor identify, then we see the compulsive drinker or addict. The problem manifests itself in the alcoholic or drug addict who secretly maintains large numbers of omnipotent and omniscient fantasies as well as many openly expressed superiority feelings in addition to uncontrollable impulse to drink or take drugs. The contrast between the addicts' magical and superman expectations and the extreme degradation in which they often find themselves following a binge produces such humiliation and guilt that they make resolutions to abandon the addiction—without notable success.

In another context, Rado says that "the grandiose conception of self is the factor that makes the craving uncontrollable. The addict believes that 'nothing can happen to me.' Though his powers of reasoning and judgment appear to be otherwise unimpaired, he believes unshakably in his personal invulnerability and immortality. His image of himself as an omnipotent and indestructible giant must be clinically described as a thinly veiled narcotic delusion of grandeur." Other authors conclude that addiction occurs in individuals who are predisposed to the response of grandiosity through retention of primordial feelings of the omnipotent self.

Some obsessives do not drink at all, or only very sparingly, when it happens to be part of their "not to" compulsion. They fear that if they drink at all, they may go to extremes. Thus they build pride around their capacity to limit their drinking and to "hold their liquor well." However, their grandiose claims, which are not always maintained, periodically produce sufficient humiliation to require narcotizing and hence the addict's binge. Clearly this is not the entire picture, but in a complete understanding of the addict the central role of grandiosity needs to be recognized.

COMPULSIVE GAMBLING

The issue of grandiosity is also evident in the compulsive gambler, who periodically engages in gambling sprees and cannot control his participation even at the risk of jeopardizing his family relationships, his profession, and even his life. When he becomes involved in a game he has no choice but to continue until he is either broke or has "broken the bank." His participation is compulsive and he cannot freely choose to leave the game. A typical obsessive-compulsive personality lies behind such behavior, and the individual's grandiose expectations are that he will win everything and lose nothing. He never expects to lose and always assumes that he can risk anything because he is protected and privileged and will ultimately win. Such attitudes are strikingly similar to those of the alcoholic or drug addict who does not expect to be influenced unduly by the whiskey or the drug and insists that he can control the intake if he wishes. The gambler also insists that he can control his risks. Like the alcoholic, he may risk his home and his job in his uncontrollable orgy of gambling. In spite of the evidence that he can lose, since he frequently does, he moves into each game with the conviction that he is certain to win. While he is abashed after each orgy, his shame and humiliation do not restrain his compulsion. The anxiety which sets off the compulsion to gamble is often a feeling of despair and hopelessness about one's self and one's fortunes and the impossibility of achieving some success through ordinary channels. The gambler cannot accept the slow climb to status but hopes to achieve it in one magical moment, without the necessary output of energy. It will all be achieved through the magic of immediate fulfillment. Such anxieties prompt him to risk his fortune and his status to achieve that magical moment which must surely come. He can exert no limit upon himself except those that are imposed by others. He is not gambling to make money. Like the alcoholic who frequently does not enjoy his drinking, he often does not enjoy the sport. His gambling is an obsessive device to relieve anxiety and to reassure himself of his special, privileged position. That it fails to do so only leaves him with the certainty that it will succeed the next time. During the game he is triumphant and about to actualize his grandiose claims and privileged self. Like the alcoholic and drug addict, he is caught in a web of obsessive necessity that he cannot escape except through a recognition of the basic problem.

COMPULSIVE MASTURBATION

There are many other compulsive pieces of behavior that might not get to the attention of others because they are private and do not involve antisocial activities. Yet they are equally as demanding and distressing as other addictions. Compulsive masturbation, for example, can become extremely disconcerting in its imperious demands upon the individual. It is quite different from the masturbatory activity in which most people indulge. Under the circumstances of a compulsion, masturbation may need to take place many times a day. When the pressure mounts and the person must masturbate to relieve the tension, he may need to do so even under unfavorable or dangerous circumstances. The person cannot resist or postpone the act.

The compulsive masturbater rarely masturbates to relieve sexual tension. He is himself fully aware of this, as the impetus to masturbate is infrequently stimulated by erotic fantasies. The need generally arises for unknown reasons and cannot be resisted. The individual is *compelled* to masturbate and while this may relieve his tense state temporarily, it often leaves him even more tense and uncomfortable.

The grandiose elements associated with this compulsion are often expressed in the fantasies that accompany the act. When masturbation is a substitute for normal sex activity the individual, being uncertain about his potency, may avoid the test of hetero-sexual activity and thus be able to maintain the grandiose illusion about his great sexual prowess. This symptom, like other com-pulsions, does not have any specific significance. Rather it reflects a general obsessive-compulsive personality structure, despite the formulation of a psychoanalyst who describes compulsive mastur-bation as "serving the purpose of protecting a passive-dependent ego from the separation anxiety caused by active sadistic phallic impulses by using the penis as a fetishistic representation of the phallic mother."

The type of compulsion that is found in an individual has some reference to his earlier experience as well as to his genetic endowment. However, the problem of the *choice* of compulsion —like the choice of symptoms in general—is still largely an un-solved one.

OBESITY

While the compulsive elements in certain types of obesity are very evident, in others they may not be so obvious. Assess-ment is difficult because such individuals generally engage in their compulsive eating orgies in secret. Unlike the alcoholic or the drug addict, the obese person rarely displays antisocial or obnoxious behavior. Psychologically, he is an addict—and the psycho-logical aspects of his addiction are similar to those of the alcoholic or drug addict. Like many alcoholics, compulsive eaters are "secret imbibers" and publicly eat so little that one is often astonished at their obesity. This tends to support the popular justification of the fat man who says he suffers from glandular trouble. While the obese person is delighted to accept this label from his friends, who never see him overeat, he knows full well where the trouble lies—even though he may also insist on a "glandular" diagnosis from his physician. While he strenuously avoids a direct confrontation with his addiction and hopes for magical cures with pills, exercise, diets or hypnosis, he is, on another level, fully aware of the compulsive nature of his overeating. Compulsive eaters are not simply overeaters; neither are they people who are chronically but slightly overweight. They are strikingly different from those who overeat because of a metabolic disorder or a thyroid deficiency. The overeating problem currently plagues a large number of Americans and citizens of other affluent countries. This situation is the result of eating and drinking in excess of the metabolic possibilities of the individual so that there is a gradual accumulation of weight. The compulsive eater is one who is *driven* and who is incapable of limiting or controlling his intake of food, so that he becomes grossly overweight. He is compelled to eat in the same way that the alcoholic or the drug addict has no choice in his addiction. The compulsive eater is pressed, not by taste or hunger, but by inner drives that he can neither understand nor control. Unlike the eater who eats too much because he likes and enjoys his food, the compulsive eater often stuffs and gorges to a point of illness. Ordinary overeating is often associated with festive events in the midst of jolly company—good food and drink in an atmosphere of good fellowship and companionship. The atmosphere adds to the enjoyment and may increase the intake of food. The compulsive eater, on the other hand, eats in secret and eats whatever is at hand—feeling somewhat sly and guilty, yet unable to abandon his misadventure. The eating proceeds in a ritualistic fashion and sometimes he may read while eating in order to avoid recognizing his excessiveness. Generally, he proceeds to eat everything at hand in an ordered fashion and the eating ritual is like other rituals of the compulsive syndrome. It is carried out without understanding, purpose, or need, and may have some meaning in a magical context. Excessive eating has always been heavily loaded with moralistic and derogatory connotations and the victims were and still are labelled pigs and gluttons and considered sinful in a Christian theology. Overeating was considered abusing one's person and was thought to be one of the cardinal sins. While obesity in females did not always involve social disapproval in terms of aesthetics, as it did in recent years in Western culture, it has usually been recognized to be a medical hazard and a handicap. However, it was not considered to be a psychological problem—similar to touching, dressing, or performing other acts as compulsive rituals. Overeating was considered to be the consequences of weakness, sinfulness, and inadequate self-control, while a hand-washing ritual might be quickly identified as abnormal mental behavior. Moralistic attitudes toward obesity have clouded the understanding of the obsessional factors involved, and have therefore hampered therapy.

Obesity is neither a moral problem nor a matter of a healthy resolve and weak will. The compulsive eater is an addict. The occasions for his addictive binges are invariably involved with anxiety—whether it is manifested or not—and are frequently initiated by hurt pride, humiliation, and feelings of rejection or isolation. These feelings are generally the outcome of a failure to live up to the person's own grandiose expectations of himself rather than the expressed disappointment of other people. Under such conditions he may engage in eating bouts of unrestrained and unlimited proportions. He will often eat until he is physically exhausted. Since he is ashamed of the quantity consumed, he prefers to eat secretly and in isolation. Often he will repress or simply forget the eating binge, especially when it may take place at odd times such as in the middle of the night. His denial may at times be so extreme as to suggest a schizophrenic dissociation process. The loneliness and emptiness of the compulsive eater are suggested by his symbolic attempt to swallow everything in order to fill this emptiness. Nothing must be left over, as if it would no longer be available if it were not eaten at that moment. He seems to be stocking up on caloric reserves as if the world would soon be emptied of nourishment, with no possible replacement. Coupled with this attitude is the related feeling of being entitled to all that is around and the fear of being cheated and taken advantage of. This feeling is sometimes related to early deprivation experiences but more often to grandiose expectations and claims in which the person sees himself as being worthy of total fulfillment. Similar to the competitive and envious person who watches what other people get to make certain that he is not short-changed, the obese person may overeat to make sure that he does not get cheated. The eating may often take place in an atmosphere of rebellion, in which he feels that he is entitled to special rewards for having been previously denied. The rebelliousness may be in response to praise if the person interprets the praise as insufficient, phony, or tricky. One 300-pound patient regularly overate when her husband told her that she looked fine and was losing weight. She felt that his remarks were phony and designed to mislead her, since she knew she was still overeating. Her husband did not know her true, inner, secret life, and she felt hopeless about his capacity to see through her even when she did not divulge that inner life.

The capacity for self-deception and the delusional distortions of the self-image of the obese person can be striking phenomena. Calories don't count—if someone else does not see them consumed. In this way obese people can convince themselves that they have eaten sparsely. The self-deception is aided by the grandiose assumption that, for them, excess carbohydrates are not stored as fat. They may express astonishment at this biochemical fact—even though they are fully aware of it on another level of conceptualization.

One 350-pound patient who came for treatment because of marital problems looked at herself in the nude regularly, noting her slim and graceful lines and openly admiring her lovely figure. She claimed that she ate very little at mealtimes, and could not understand her overweight. Her husband was convinced that she did not overeat except on infrequent occasions, when he would inadvertently awaken early in the morning to find his wife gorging on huge sandwiches, cokes, cakes, and candies. This happened with far greater frequency than he was ever aware of. The defense of denial may often reach psychotic proportions. Such people feel that they live prudent, mildly uncontrolled lives. Hilde Bruch has noted in her classic studies on obesity that the self-image of the obese person is often that of a thin person who will starve unless he continues to eat. It is the converse of the anorexia nervosa patient who is extraordinarily thin and refuses to eat because his self-image is that of an obese person who will become grossly ugly unless he controls his food intake. At times the obese person may have a delusion of being denied nourishment by a hostile world, or of being destroyed by worms which demand a constant intake of food. The schizophrenic qualities of the disorder are often clearly manifest and the element of denial is often a crucial factor in the therapy of obesity, as it is with alcoholics.

The underlying character structure of the obese person is like that of other addicts. The compulsive incapacity to control the food intake is related to the over-all problem of control in other areas of living. Such people are pressed by their uncertainties and feelings of helplessness and impotence; they display a wide variety of obsessive symptoms. They are caught up in attempts at perfection and invulnerability, and have a need at all times to control their own actions as well as those of others. For example, one moderately obese compulsive eater refused to acknowledge her approaching menopause. She said that she was not ready for it and had not decided she wanted it yet. She was desperately searching for approval and while her activity was directed toward controlling others, she tried to justify her behavior by insisting that she was just a puppet in the hands of her husband. There was no real conviction about losing weight since she had not yet decided that she was fat. Thus she denied her overeating, except at rare moments of self-awareness which fitted into her grandiose conception of omnipotence and superiority. This patient had many phobias and somatic obsessional preoccupations. Her communication difficulties were classically obsessional. She obscured all her statements with qualifications and needed to explain each one so that she never got to the point of her story. She was evasive, distracting, and indecisive. Although she wanted very much to lose weight and reestablish some of her earlier attractiveness, she maintained that she could not exert the proper degree of self-control to achieve it.

Her usual indecisiveness made her swing back and forth in her resolution to diet, and at times of stress she would overeat as a rebellious gesture against her husband. At the bottom of her difficulty was the grandiose picture of herself, which would not allow her to admit that she could not control her overeating. As a superior, godlike person, she expected that she should be loved for what she was and should not need to conform to any conventional ideas of beauty. She considered herself exempt from caloric issues and insisted that the foods that made others fat should not bother her. She never related the issues of calorie count to weight because she considered herself superhuman and beyond the natural laws of digestion.

The same issue was demonstrated in a 285-pound compulsive eater who was tall and had attractive features, but was gross in her appearance. Her compulsive eating was complicated by a tendency toward stealing. She was a marked manipulator whose activities were invariably involved in controlling others, yet she appeared to be entirely at the mercy of others.

Her eating was done in secret and in the evenings, and she was mainly unaware of the quantity of her intake. On these occasions she gorged herself, although she was extremely restrained in the presence of her family. In this way she engaged their sympathy, since they were impressed by her sparse appetite and felt her obesity was not her fault. She was rigid, stubborn, and rebellious. To avoid being "pushed around" she went to the opposite extreme of refusing to budge an inch once she made up her mind. At the other times, she refused to make a decision for fear she might be pushed to change it. Her eating problem was tied up with her capacity for denial and, at times, she was firmly convinced that she was not fat. Every positive comment from her husband was translated as affirmation of her attractive figure, even though she could not really trust or believe him. She managed to force him to compliment her, but when he did she became angry and overate because she felt his comments were not freely given. While her obesity forced her into treatment, she came only upon the insistence of her husband. She did not deal with her obesity for a long time after she began therapy. She directed her communications to many other areas. During this period she unwittingly managed to expose the whole range of her obsessional symptoms, which made her overeating understandable. In addition to her obesity, she had a compulsion to steal.

Relationship to Kleptomania

She managed to avoid mentioning stealing and to deny it as part of her living until she was arrested—even though her need to shop-lift anything portable was ever-present. While the things she took did not have any utility or intrinsic value, she justified her behavior by a Robin Hood fantasy of stealing from the rich to help the poor. She was quite well off financially and could comfortably fill all the needs of her family. Her stealing was rationally unmotivated and could be understood only in terms of her inability to pass up anything that she could get for nothing. If it was there to be had, she felt she was entitled to it. She never considered the consequences of her behavior because it never occurred to her that she would get caught. She secretly viewed herself as a superhuman person whose grandiose self could outwit and outmanipulate anyone in the world. Thus she had never even considered the possibility of being caught.

She felt that shoplifting was a virtue and a positive achievement and that it would be cheating her family not to steal. She viewed this as her job, just as her husband had his job. It was an extraordinary defense, typical of many compulsive justifications in which the compulsion is visualized as a virtue. In this instance, however, it had antisocial consequences.

Kleptomania raises the question of why some compulsions

direct the person to antisocial acts while others produce effects which are destructive only to the individual involved. The compulsion itself is amoral and is the result of a defensive process. The direction of the compulsion and its acceptability by the culture is determined by the ethos of that culture and is not innate in the symptom itself. The compulsion to peep (voyeurism), or the compulsion to expose oneself may have severe consequences in one culture and be relatively unnoticed in another. The compulsion's origins may have some basis in the mores of the culture, but the person himself may not respond to his acts as being immoral. On the other hand, some compulsions which may not antagonize or be abhorrent to the culture may be entirely unacceptable to the person himself. This is true, for example, of compulsive eating or obsessive preoccupations of a hostile or sexual nature. While it involves moral issues, the compulsion can be understood only in psychological terms—even though our ability to treat some compulsions is often thwarted by the legal consequences of the behavior.

For the patient described above, stealing was her contribution to the household and she felt proud, rather than contrite and ashamed. While she recognized the distortions in her explanation and the compulsive nature of her stealing, she was extremely reluctant to connect her kleptomania with her compulsive eating. Yet she could see similarity in her grandiose expectations of exemption and special privilege in both areas. She felt guilty about both her eating and stealing only when they were brought to her attention. Her rationalization that she was serving others and the denial and evasiveness are familiar defenses against anxieties. However, the relationship to anxiety is neither simple nor direct. It is not that she steals or overeats when she becomes noticeably anxious or upset; it is frequently the opposite. The relationship is a much more subtle one and concerns the uncertainty of her acceptability and desirability, which may be stirred up by many things—including praise and compliments. Her compulsive symptoms derive from her needs to prove, justify, and document a superior and omnipotent self which will guarantee her future security.

Thus on the one occasion when she was apprehended, she did not appear crushed or chastised; rather, she considered it an unexpected error in her usual impregnable and grandiose self. She thought it was the result of carelessness caused by a headache and that it would not happen again. At the time of her apprehension she attempted to evade the responsibility for her behavior by telling the authorities that she was not stealing, but was gathering material for a short story. This fantasy was sufficiently reworked so that when she related it she more than half believed it. She also maintained that her shoplifting was a creative task, which, when she wrote her account of it, would be a boon to humanity for which she should be rewarded. So certain was she of her immunity that she never really expected the storekeeper to prosecute. She simply did not see the event as a crime, but only as a mistake.

When the trial date was set, instead of feeling restrained she went on a shoplifting binge. Instead of trying to impress the court with spotless behavior before the trial, she determined to get as much as possible before it became known publicly that she had shoplifted. She dealt with the incident as a minor error and continued trying to rework the plot so that she would end up as a heroine in the eyes of her family, although she actually took great care that they learn nothing about the matter.

As a result of this incident and of my active interest in her during this period, the therapeutic work advanced considerably. We managed to explore the intricacies of her obesity as well as the kleptomania. She was able to examine her grandiosity in a most direct way and described several occasions that she had previously forgotten. The first was an early experience when she had played God, and in an authoritarian manner relieved a neighboring woman of witches and ghosts. The neighbor treated her with great awe from then on. The patient then began to believe in her omnipotence and on several occasions tried to take over a hospital ward and cure a friend. She finally had to be asked to leave as she was disrupting the hospital routine by countering the doctors' orders. She recognized that these grandiose assumptions were related to her need to be omniscient and omnipotent, as her early life had been one of marked uncertainty about herself and her future. She was able to see the connection between this occasion and her secret expectations of God-like exemption from the natural laws of biology or the social laws concerning stealing. She became aware that her inability to recognize any danger or guilt was a result of her grandiosity; she also began to see the realistic consequences of her behavior on herself and her family.

As a result of her therapy she now has only occasional temptations to steal, particularly when the items are small and can be considered necessary. However, she has managed to restrain these feelings most of the time. Her stealing is less compulsive and she has some choice in the matter. An understanding of risk, danger, guilt, etc., now enters into her calculations and she must decide between the danger of being caught and the pleasure of getting away with it. She is still less motivated by moral considerations than by practical ones, and still has some doubt about whether she does or does not have a right to steal. While her grandiose state has been punctured, it has not disappeared. The automatic, unplanned, and unprogrammed stealing has, on the whole, diminished—even though she still has strong feelings of invulnerability and the capacity to pull off the perfect job. After several years' therapy, she moved to another city. Though her kleptomania was much reduced, her obesity was not. It was as if practical necessity of a more dramatic kind took precedence over the cosmetic aspects of her problem.

From the point of view of the problem related here, however, the patient demonstrated very clearly the relationship between grandiosity and particular symptoms such as kleptomania and obesity. The connection lies in the concept of the compulsive drive, in which compulsive behavior is directly related to grandiosity. From this point of view, the problem of grandiosity is considered to be more essential to the therapeutic process than the previously held relationships of kleptomania or obesity to sexual problems. The symbolic significance of stealing as a sexual transformation is not borne out in the observations of this woman.

Her sexual difficulties appeared to have no relation to her kleptomania.

Similarly, there are several problems the understanding of which could be greatly advanced by taking into account grandiosity. The psychopathic personality and the dynamics of paranoid states are intimately involved with the issues. While the relationship to the addictions is unclear, there are many common threads.

PARANOID STATES

The omnipotent and grandiose tendencies that are consistently present in the paranoid state were explained by Freud as reflecting the result of the paranoid's feeling of being especially selected for malevolence and attention. This feeling of specialness and significance is then enhanced to a grandiose state. In this connection, Freud said: "The development of megalomania is thus attributed to a process which we may describe as rationalization. But to ascribe such important affective influences to a rationalization is, it seems to us, an entirely unpsychological procedure." In this view, the paranoid state precedes the development of grandiosity and is responsible for it. This concept is quite superficial and, as Freud himself recognized, an "unpsychological procedure" with which to explain such a significant development. This is particularly true when one recognizes that grandiosity occurs quite commonly in situations other than paranoid development. A more generalized theory of grandiosity not only should explain the condition's development in paranoids but also should be capable of explaining its role in other psychiatric disorders.

We find paranoid ideation in practically everyone except the most secure and mature individuals. However, when a true paranoid development occurs, the special sense of privilege and being superhuman is reflected in the feeling of grandiosity which becomes delusional and can be part of a schizophrenic disorder.

There is much evidence that the grandiosity which develops out of the obsessional disease is responsible for the paranoid development. The response of the community to the exaggerated claims and demands of the grandiose paranoid are rarely friendly or compliant, and are in fact usually angry and rejecting. The soil from which the grandiose feelings develop was already nourished with doubts, fears, and uncertainties. Thus the unfriendly, rejecting, and at times hostile reaction of the environment tends to provoke and stimulate paranoid ideas.

Several case histories will demonstrate such a development. An obsessional young lady in a grandiose excitement claimed to be one of the four best writers in the English language. She based this claim on an unfinished manuscript which had been years in the making and which realistically supplied no basis for such an appraisal. She was an extremely insecure person, overburdened by a succession of phobic and compulsive rituals. Under great stress she would become quite excited and would openly express many of her grandiose claims, which she secretly nourished even while derogating herself.

Another patient took me to task for assuming that his boss, who was an outstanding authority in his field and 20 years the patient's senior, was necessarily better informed about the job than was he. The patient felt that the realistic situation did not necessarily prove this contention because no one yet knew what he, the patient, was capable of. He refused to take into account the factor of experience, additional education, and background. All the patient offered was the remote—but "correct" in the strict sense—notion that he still might be better at the task if he were magically and suddenly transported into it. His insistence in the face of numerous rational factors was an instance of his grandiosity. While it would be truly reassuring for the patient to recognize that he *might* achieve his boss' position in due time, and that it would be impossible to expect to be in it at this stage of his development, he preferred to consider the situation in the most far-fetched ways in order to maintain his grandiosity. He explained the boss' position in terms of politics, accident of birth, and a collusion of immoral and unfair practices.

Another example illustrates the relation of obsession and paranoia, as well as grandiosity. It deals with a 45-year-old man who grew up the middle child of three sons. He was treated with special care, but also derided because of his physical incapacities. His household was chaotic and completely hypercritical. The Christian virtues were expounded and emphasized while the father made his living in periodic illegal ventures. From a very early age the patient experienced severe anxieties in his family relationships and spent most of his time trying fruitlessly to impress the family with his capacity and skill. He soon outshone his family in intellectual pursuits, but this failed to stimulate their admiration and respect. In early childhood he developed many phobias and compulsive ritualistic behavior patterns which elicited the family's derision. At first he followed the family design for his career, but soon abandoned it for a career in science. Although he felt successful, his financial reward was small.

He began therapy when he was almost immobilized by a complicated succession of compulsive rituals ranging from washing routines to activities surrounding his work life. All his work had to be letter-and-comma perfect, so that he might redo it dozens of times. These rituals, when interspersed with obsessional preoccupations arising from past incidents and recent events, made his life an impossible hurdle. He could work only against the greatest odds and at times could do nothing at all except to perform the obsessional demands made upon him.

With regard to the issue of grandiosity, he became very angry on occasion when he assumed that I thought a piece of research which had won a prize was better than the one he had submitted. His rationalization regarding his failure to win the prize consisted essentially in tearing down the winning project, with which he was not even familiar, and accusing the judges of being ignorant and prejudiced. He recognized his inability to accept any kind of second-best position, and after some discussion he appeared to accept the observations about his obsessional demands. Several weeks later, however, he expressed great anger and annoyance and insisted that the therapy was trying to sell him on the notion of grandiosity when everything was clearly a matter of his being factually superior. He introduced more evidence of the prize winner's being incapable, and tried to prove that in this instance he should have won. He accused me of siding with his enemies and pushing him around. He not only defended his grandiose claims but expressed great disappointment and anger that the overvalued judgment of himself was not accepted by others.

We explored his rationalizations and other defensive devices which were designed to force me and others to accept his point of view. It became clear that his intense need to win and his inability to accept any other judgment but his own was involved in this crisis. I added in the course of our exploration that it was clear that his failure to win was neither shameful nor disappointing. While it certainly would have been preferable if he had won, it would not necessarily make him more acceptable. Therapy was not judging his talent but examining his way of life. It finally became clear to him that he could not admit defeat in this instance because he felt I expected him to win and would reject him and dispose of him as a patient unless he was superior and outstanding. His failure to win the prize would be interpreted as an indication of his mediocrity. This incident was very revealing to the patient. It demonstrated his grandiosity and his defenses against it, and illuminated the obsessive pattern and its adaptive function very clearly.

PSYCHOPATHIC PERSONALITY

Grandiosity is also related to a character disorder called "psychopathic personality." In these people, however, addictive qualities in their behavior are more easily demonstrated. Earlier explanations involved the contradiction of a person who feels no guilt or suffers no remorse and yet is looking for punishment. This interpretation required the hypothesis of a death instinct, or the concept of an unconscious feeling of guilt. Yet the psychopathic personality moves about in the community in every walk of life, often very successfully, and is brought before justice by society only when he commits illegal acts. The type of behavior that constitutes the core of this illness is related to the inability of such individuals to make any deep, meaningful relationships—even when they are often actively involved in social affairs. They do not get emotionally involved in positive terms and they exploit every relationship they have. They seem conscienceless, devoid of shame and remorse, and *appear* to feel no guilt for any of their antisocial behavior. When apprehended they may make fervent pleas for forgiveness or promise never to repeat such behavior—but invariably they do repeat it. They seem not to benefit either from punishment or previous experiences. For these reasons they sometimes appear stupid, though actually they generally have high I.Q.'s and are usually clever and "brilliant operators." They trade on their charm and capacity to deceive and are extremely successful in taking advantage of the human propensity to get something for nothing.

Generally these people appear to function well—without anxiety and seemingly without difficulty or distress. They appear to have no manifest delusions or to give other evidence of psychoses. While their relationships are cold, calculated, and without real feeling, they seem to be intense and involved. Such individuals have always posed an unusual problem for psychiatrists. They seem to be quite normal, even when their behavior has been illegal, reproachful, or openly hostile and deceitful. One psychiatrist has described them as wearing "masks of sanity."

There have been various attempts to explain the psychopathic personality's behavior by the notion of a deficient superego or conscience. It was assumed that because their repetitive behavior made it certain that they would be apprehended by the authorities that this was an indication of their desire to be caught and punished. While all agree that such people do not seem to benefit from punishment, some theorists hold the "deficient super ego" view and explain it either by the death instinct or the unconscious need for punishment. However, they do not clarify why someone pushes himself into getting punishment when he can neither benefit from it nor enjoy it. Other explanations for this behavior are in order.

One notion about the psychopath is that he does not experience anxiety. While it is generally agreed that anxiety is not ordinarily manifested by such a person in a direct way, it is clear that he is not only capable of experiencing anxiety but that the anxiety can be sufficiently severe to warrant the most stringent defenses in order to cope with it. The psychopath's anxiety is usually expressed in indirect ways, such as in hectic, compulsive behavior—especially when he feels himself in danger of being discovered or exposed. When one would expect outbursts of anxiety—that is, when he is actually discovered, apprehended, or convicted—he seems to display the least anxiety. It is as if, at these times, he utilizes the defense of denial against his anxiety. Keeping this in mind, many things seem understandable about the psychopath.

The psychopathic personality, like all other psychiatric syndromes, is the consequence of a series of defensive maneuvers which are designed to adapt to certain conditions of existence. There are many data to suggest that the personality of the psychopath may result from extreme conditions of almost total rejection and indifference in the early years. In the atmosphere of cold, detached, and undoubtedly egocentric parents, the child manages through some psychological defenses to avoid psychosis and even death. Consequently, the child develops such characteristics as result from survival under the most extreme circumstances—cunning, egocentricity, distrust, and emotional fluidity. In addition, he develops a collection of techniques to charm and exploit others for his own use, and with no consideration for their feelings. Thus the syndrome could be visualized as an adaptive development in which the person tries to get what he can—using guile and cunning—at the least cost to his own feelings. He behaves as though the world owes him a living. What he can achieve by trickery and deceit is valued as highly as achievements obtained by effort and hard work. Often even greater pride is taken in achievements which are the result of deceit—even when they may require more effort than more conventional behavior. It is as though the illegal and dangerous nature of an activity carries special rewards. Rebellion and nonconformity are elements in this behavior, but the atmosphere of getting something for nothing by activity which is not designed to achieve the usual results is most appealing to the psychopath. He wishes to avoid being a "sucker" like everyone else. Only unusual paths are valued—even if they are illegal or bizarre.

The psychopath's need for a guaranteed avoidance of anxiety is very strong. He achieves his goal through the technique of denial through which he refuses overtly to acknowledge his distress. While cunning and trickery are useful devices to achieve illegal goals, intelligence and a clear awareness of the weaknesses of other humans is also essential. The complicated efforts to achieve easy rewards often require a highly developed intellectual capacity and always a skilled understanding of the ways of society and the weaknesses of man and the temptations to which he is subject. With such techniques the psychopath's life proceeds with a maximum security.

Such characteristics are an essential part of the obsessive-compulsive personality. The psychopathic personality is a compulsive and perfectionistic one, and it strives for omniscience and omnipotence in order to guarantee existence. Unlike the obsessional, however, the person's anger and rebellion appear greater and more overt. Many psychopaths, however, enjoy full and successful careers because the particular medium they choose to express their psychopathy is not looked upon as illegal—for example, a fringe political or religious group.

The psychopath has a grandiosity which expands and prospers under success and which remains untouched when failure occurs. It leads him to view himself as exempt from natural causes and events and permits him to engage in the most extreme and arrogant kinds of behavior. He believes that he is invulnerable and much too clever to be caught by the police. He feels he is able to carry out the perfect crime or the faultless swindle. He has contempt for the police as well as for his victim, and it is this attitude which leads him to excesses of behavior and eventual exposure. He invariably overestimates his cunning and underestimates the capacities of the police and all others. Most of his failures arise out of foolish and arrogant errors and not from unconscious wishes for punishment. What appears to be unconscious guilt or the need for punishment is a grandiose presumption of immunity and a certainty of exemption and privilege. Psychopaths are always surprised, annoyed, and disappointed when caught. They insist that the incident was an accident. It is in this sense that they do not appear to benefit from punishment. Prison or punishment is considered an interim period; the next time he will execute his plans more efficiently. His intellectual capacity, which might win him success in almost any undertaking, is put to use in trying to get something for nothing. His intellectual skills are not freely used but are tied to the compulsive performance of shady activities.

For a short period of time I had occasion to deal with a 32-year-old male psychopath who had already spent 18 years in jail for a variety of minor crimes, mainly stealing. The last time that I saw him, he had broken into a parsonage and had stolen the poor box. He had been released from prison only 15 days before this incident, and was on his way home. He was a very bright man, with an I.Q. of over 130, and had been a teacher during his last prison term. He had gone into the parsonage and had managed to find the money, but on his way out he tripped over a chair and the resulting clatter brought the police. The robbery was unplanned and was done on the spur of the moment. He felt that he had taken every precaution in selecting this target, and in not making any commotion or drawing attention to himself. However, he said he did not need to plan any of his crimes; stealing was easy and all the odds were on the side of the thief. He never expected to get caught. He stated that he learned from each crime how to do it better the next time—but he suggested that he might not be around long enough to be really perfect. He described a compulsive need to steal that manifested signs usually associated with alcoholism. His grandiose fantasies all involved being more clever than the authorities and secretly expecting this to be acknowledged by them. His previous imprisonments had no effect whatsoever upon him, except to justify his grievances and to polish up his plans for further jobs.

The grandiosity of the psychopath is one level removed from the grandiose delusions in all psychoses, in which the individual attempts to actualize his grandiosity and insists that he is the exalted, privileged, and exempt individual. Many of the phenomena associated with the psychoses, including suicide, can often be understood as the result of grandiose illusions through which the person feels immune from the laws of nature and expects no consequences from his extreme behavior. Grandiosity often accompanies the manic state. In such cases, the exuberant, intensely overactive and, at times, creative performances frequently lead the person to presume powers which he does not possess. These fantasies are the direct result of an enormous output of energy which may produce an unusual amount of activity. The person misconstrues quantity for quality and assumes a competence far beyond his resources. The grandiosity is not a rationalization for his uniqueness; rather, it is his mania which manifests itself in a plethora of performances that resemble a massive skill that is misinterpreted by the patient. The grandiosity becomes a defense against the doubts and uncertainties that lie a mere fraction below the surface. It can easily be punctured and deflated—leaving the manic hurt, angry, irritable, and frequently depressed.

In the schizophrenic psychoses we find a variety of backgrounds for the grandiose states that may be involved in the illness. At times they are part of a paranoid development in which the initial problem appears to be a grandiose development designed to deal with a severely damaged ego structure and a failing self-esteem. Such a possible failure endangers the person with feelings of disintegration and humiliation. The grandiose state may be the bulwark that prevents panic and utter destruction. The grandiose presumptions are rarely shared by the community and are generally scoffed at. This stimulates the conviction of a malevolent, destructive environment that requires caution and extreme vigilence, and may quickly lead to a paranoid state in which malevolence is expected and anticipated —and finally openly expressed in words and behavior. On the other hand, grandiosity may be the outcome of a catatonic withdrawal during which the person is engaged in an assortment of world-shaking fantasies and delusions. The alternative is either annihilation or hebephrenic deterioration. The severe low esteem which produces a schizophrenic withdrawal often demands a massive reorganization by means of a grandiose elaboration which brings the person to the opposite extreme: an omnipotent giant guaranteed against all the threats and anxieties of living. Three vignettes highlight this issue.

Following a severe depression, a minister became hypermanic and began working 14 to 16 hours a day, visiting his parishioners, lecturing, preaching, and covering an enormous amount of territory in his parish. This sudden increase in zeal and devotion made him decide that he had made contact with Christ, and he began to believe that he had been chosen for great work. His grandiosity expanded to the point of assuming that he was eternal and without illness or disease. He threw away his glasses and claimed that he no longer needed any sleep. The exhaustion and near-blindness which followed soon led to some paranoid elaborations about the envy of his fellow clergymen. The paranoia soon became more prominent and his behavior became hostile rather than benevolent; he required hospitalization.

A young woman decided that she was a writer of great note. This followed a series of growing crises about her writing, which was not proceeding very well. She decided that she was being recorded all the time in order that her pearls of wisdom be captured. She soon began suspecting everyone, particularly her husband, who, she felt, was derogating her. The grandiose delusions produced a series of embarrassing situations which nec-

essitated removing her from her friends. Her grandiosity sub-
sided under tranquilizing drugs and psychoanalytic therapy that
was directed at exploring the necessity for such a massive defensive system.

Following a trip to New York, a young man was slowly
becoming alienated and isolated from his family and friends.
On his trip he had begun to ruminate about the Cold War and
had decided upon a solution. It was a complicated, typically
obsessive program which he was determined to bring to the
President immediately. The grandiose response followed a growing deterioration in his mental condition and a great deal of
anxiety about it. He was becoming fearful of a mental breakdown, and the grandiose solution was an attempt at reconstruction that overshot the mark.

PART III

treatment

CHAPTER 9

Therapy of the Obsessive
Personality

The essential task in the therapy of the obsessive-compulsive disorders, or in dealing
with the obsessional dynamisms in other personality disorders,
is that of conveying insight and initiating learning and change
without getting caught in the "obsessional tug-of-war," a term
that describes obsessional behavior which results in hostile and
antagonistic exchanges with others.

As with all neurotic difficulties, the work lies in the identification, clarification, and finally, in the alteration of the defensive patterns which maintain the neurosis. Such progress becomes
possible when the patient's self-esteem or ego strength becomes
sufficiently strengthened to withstand the major assaults against
his defenses. While the problems that brought about the obsessional defenses are comparatively easy to uncover, the defensive
structure which develops around these issues are most difficult
to unravel. At times the particular issues of the patient are

obvious and plainly stated in his obsessional ruminations or his compulsive rituals. For example, a ritualistic avoidance of knives may be a clear statement within the awareness of the patient that he has some uneasiness about losing control of his hostile impulses. Thus the identification of the problem—which is the fear of loss of control of his hostile impulses—is simple enough. However, it is soon evident that it is not only a fear of injuring someone else that is involved but rather a generalized uneasiness and uncertainty about the possibility of losing control in general, or of being unable to control oneself at all times.

It is paradoxical that in the attempts to clarify an obsessional's life, the issues become more complicated and confused. Ordinarily, increasing one's knowledge of a particular problem helps to focus on the relevant components. In dealing with the obsessional, however, new issues and qualifications of the old ones tend to broaden the inquiry. It often appears as though the patient were deliberately confusing the situation by introducing new issues when there is real danger of clarifying something. Actually, he is trying to be precise and to avoid making errors. The additional factors are generally raised as he gets close to seeing his responsibility or failure in some activity. Before he is ready to accept an observation about some matter in which he played a responsible role, he tries to involve every possibility outside himself. Therefore it looks as if he does this purposefully, as these new factors often lead the investigation into a cul-de-sac from which no fruitful return is possible.

In order to obtain some value from such a development, once it has occurred, the therapist must go back to the beginning of the exchange and retrace it carefully—noting where the extraneous or vaguely relevant matters were introduced by the patient. It is only rarely that this sort of unraveling can take place outside of therapy. Ordinarily, one is left with a feeling of hopelessness and helplessness when one gets caught in a conversation which appears to be moving in one direction and suddenly shifts just as one approaches the destination. Attempts to retrace the path generally lead to further digression. Usually the other party simply withdraws altogether. It is this activity that causes the obsessional to be referred to as "slippery" or "elusive" —it is so hard to pin him down.

In therapy it is imperative that such communication entanglements be worked through so that the patient can see exactly what he does and how he defeats attempts at understanding. He must recognize that while he may not do this deliberately, it nevertheless occurs frequently and regularly. The therapist must retrace the conversation and point out every new digression as it developed. He must resist all temptations to follow every lead and every rationalization; he must stick to the point in following through this particular gambit. Recording sessions can be very useful in this regard, but the compulsiveness of the therapist (which would be required to record all the sessions) may outweigh the advantages gained by the patient, who can hear just how he frustrates clarity even while he is searching for clarification.

It is inevitable that the therapist will occasionally get caught in the "fly paper" of the obsessional's way of life, and he must recognize it as quickly as possible so as to avoid as much of it as he can. The patient gets a sense of power out of these exchanges, in which his verbal gymnastics serve to frustrate the therapist.

The above situation is illustrated by the following vignette: A patient expressed irritation at her husband because he became abusive about the driver in front of him. Her husband countered by saying that the driver was a poor one who was endangering himself as well as others. Besides, he asked, why did she always defend the other person and attack him? She stated that her concern was with his behavior because he was her husband. He charged her with being an appeaser and with failing to criticize others even when it was deserved. He referred to another occasion when, at a party, she had agreed with a guest who was obviously wrong in order to avoid a heated argument. She replied that she didn't want the party to break up—she was not just being an appeaser, she was just more socially adept than he.

At this he accused her of being a phoney and of going over-board to be nice to others when she didn't really mean it. The issue had now moved from his irritable, egocentric behavior to her passive, compliant tendencies, and, if it did not get inter-rupted either by tantrums or sullen withdrawal by either of them, could extend far into the night, ranging from attack to counterattack as each one's sensitivities got touched upon. The ludicrousness of such an argument is more easily noted by an observer than by the participants.

It is clear in the above account that the subject was changed in the course of the exchange. At the outset, the husband was criticized, but when he counterattacked she was left defending herself. Generally, the patient's emotions are running so high and the need to win and overwhelm the other is so great that there is. little chance of a logical or clear semantic analysis of the situation. When the partner also has some obsessional prob-lems, the "stickiness" is compounded and only havoc can result. One can see how each step gets the original issue mixed in with additional issues until it is simply lost sight of.

It is necessary to face this aspect of the obsessional's diffi-culties early in the therapeutic work. The most effective way of countering it is by a slow, set-by-step unraveling process, as indicated above, wherein the actual side-stepping techniques are uncovered and brought to the patient's attention. The obfus-cating tendencies can then be recognized and acknowledged.

The patient must have a minimum of trust in the therapist and a willingness to accept the role of patient for the process to begin. The readiness to admit the need for help does not mean a total acceptance of another's ability to provide such help. While there are many formal requirements for the doctor-patient relationship, such as keeping appointments, paying the fees, saying whatever comes to mind—all of which can be agreed upon in advance—there are some requirements which cannot be met so easily in view of the nature of the neurotic or psychotic process. The obsessional patient will try to follow the formal requirements scrupulously. However, the more pervasive tendencies of omniscience and omnipotence, the characteristic doubts, the grandiose contempt, and the tendencies to distract will play havoc with the therapeutic process unless these matters are always kept in the forefront of the therapist's attention.

This type of patient does not deliberately sabotage the therapy; he is merely behaving as an obsessional. His behavior is not resistance nor is it a need to defeat either the therapist or the therapy; it is merely another manifestation of obsessional behavior. The therapist cannot assume or take for granted that the patient will suddenly change and stop behaving like an obsessional simply because he has agreed to enter into therapy. It would be naive to expect that a neurotic who has difficulty in coming to grips with an issue, or who procrastinates and is given to indecisiveness, will be able to commit himself quickly to a process that demands total commitment and involvement.

It will be a long time before he will be able to verbalize his doubts about himself, the therapist, and the process. It is essential that he hold himself aloof and free of entanglement and commitment so that he can avoid being hurt and humiliated. He will need to know his therapist and experience a number of incidents with him before the more subtle safeguards can be dropped and the beginnings of trust can take place. It is inevitable that a person who must know everything and never be deficient or fallible will react to treatment as a challenge or a threat. In order to learn one must be receptive as well as motivated, which means to be free of the obstacles which interfere with learning. One must be able to listen with an open mind, without immediate denial or derogation of the material presented. Therapy is a learning process which requires the active interest and participation of the patient and this is true whether one views the dynamics of cure as the result of insight, genetic reconstruction, resolution of transference neurosis, reconditioning, corrective emotional experience, or simple relearning. Therefore not only is it necessary to motivate the patient to explore his way of living in order to discover the inappropriate patterns of behavior and their sources, but it is also necessary to interest and encourage him to take steps to change his way of life. This requires a therapist who can demand participation without challenging or stirring up the patient's opposition. The patient must acquire sufficient trust, self-esteem, and readiness to take some risks and face the possibility of failure.

All of the above poses particular difficulties for the obsessional. In addition to his learning problems there are often insurmountable obstacles in attempting to try out new ways of functioning. Since most of the obsessional patterns of behavior arise from feelings of powerlessness and uncertainty, the patient finds it particularly threatening to try out new solutions unless he can have some guarantees and expectations of success. In spite of their unsatisfactory results, the old patterns are more familiar. There must be strong incentives to attempt new solutions.

Understanding that the obsessional needs to control and that the nature of therapeutic relationship puts him in a dependent role, the therapist must acknowledge the patient's defiance and discomfort as a natural outcome of his neurotic demands. Because of these dependency problems, the therapeutic relationship should not be of an authoritarian type if it is to succeed. However, the very structure of the psychoanalytic situation tends to encourage a development in which the therapist is the leader, the teacher, and the person who has an "in" on what's happening. The patient is the pupil who is forced to depend on the ministrations of the magic man who sets the rules of the game. Such an atmosphere may tend to produce an outwardly compliant attitude with an inwardly resistive and negativistic defense. The obsessional ordinarily proceeds only by being forced —either by circumstances or strong pressures—to overcome his indecisive ruminations. While he needs pushing, he nevertheless resents it and insists that he be allowed to act on his own, free from compulsion. Therefore, the therapist may be caught in a double bind if he takes a strong hand to forestall the controlling tendencies of the patient while allowing sufficient space for maneuvering so that the patient is permitted to decide on matters for himself. For any useful work to grow out of the therapeutic relationship, the prevailing atmosphere must be one of freedom—with a lack of compulsion and authority, with a minimum of rules and rituals, and a maximum of exchange, in which the rights and limits of both parties are clearly understood. For the patient to perceive clearly his patterns of operation, the therapeutic atmosphere must not parallel the life experiences of the obsessional. In every respect the treatment behavior of the obsessional must be understood in its contradictory aspects in order to maintain the cooperation and participation of the patient.

The ultimate goal in therapy is to effect a change in the patient's living, not merely to induce insight. Insight is only the prelude to change; it provides the tools for the alteration in one's patterns of living. But the therapist must also assist the patient in utilizing his new understandings. This demands an approach which is less rigid and less tied up in traditional methodology. The therapist must feel free to be of active assistance in the process. Obsessional patterns which are so heavily involved with ritualistic forms of behavior cannot be resolved by therapeutic measures which are just as overloaded with ritual. The therapist must be flexible enough to try novel approaches and techniques.

The process of therapy, therefore, can only be described in general terms that leave room for considerable variation and flexibility in specific instances. Broad tendencies and characteristic maneuvers of both patient and therapist can be discussed, because the nature of the obsessional defense produces particular technical problems. However, detailed exchanges and specific interventions will vary with each patient and therapist.

Not every obsessional patient will present all the characteristics described in earlier chapters. Some elements will be more obvious and will play a more important role in one patient or be of secondary importance in another. It is the therapist's job to recognize the main themes in each case, as well as the subsidiary themes. Therapeutic emphasis must be placed on the major mechanisms, but at the same time not minimize the lesser patterns.

GENERAL PRINCIPLES

Since the therapist should not have a preconceived program, he cannot pretend irritation or act annoyed. While role-playing may be valid under certain conditions, it is not useful and may be dangerous in the therapy of obsessional states. A prior decision to avoid all intellectual discussions in therapy is also unwise since it resembles so closely the obsessional's tendency to make resolutions or plans to replace spontaneous responses. Such a decision should come out of the experiences in the process of therapy. A spontaneous bit of irritation or anger in response to a specific event can meaningfully advance the therapy. But a prescription for the therapist to express hostility in order to encourage the patient's hostile feelings or a program of provocative silence to stimulate the patient's anger may be quite detrimental.

Such controlled responses are easily idenitfied by the patient and seen as a contrived attempt to test his reactions. He may respond in a way which is expected to win approval or he may become discouraged because he feels manipulated and "on trial" instead of being engaged in a collaborative enterprise.

The obsessional person has considerable difficulty in being spontaneous or direct in the expression of his feelings. A *spontaneously* provoked response by the therapist can be very efficacious in stimulating the patient's spontaneity, although this type of approach requires a highly responsive therapist and a greater involvement and participation by him in the process. It means that the therapist must take some risks with regard to exposing some of his own weaknesses and deficiencies. As well as being able to maintain some objectivity and separateness, he must respond in human terms to the interpersonal exchanges to demonstrate to the patient that being human, fallible, and admitting to deficiencies need not result in rejection or humiliation. Instead of rejecting the therapist, the patient may have heightened respect for him—this can be an important learning experience for the patient and may encourage him to try it too. Such an approach to a patient is both difficult and uncomfortable for the therapist, but it is more interesting and fruitful for both therapist and patient. The use of humor and sarcasm in the therapy of the obsessional can be most effective too; it requires becoming involved with the patient's tendencies toward extremes and his difficulty in dealing lightly with any issues. A most effective technique in this respect is to highlight the patient's extreme positions by pressing still further, which has the effect of slapstick exaggeration and often points up the pretentiousness of the patient's superstandards. When the patient demands that every detail be precisely accurate or that impossible goals be achieved one can agree that this might be possible if the patient were indeed a combination of God, Einstein, Shakespeare, and General MacArthur. The effective use of this type of sarcasm may be more successful than hours of patient explanation and clarification. The obsessional's latent sense of humor is one of his unused capacities and to bring it out into the open and help him use it can be a most rewarding experience. The use of humor and spontaneous laughter can often break through a communication impasse.

The therapist's attempts at humor, however, are not invariably met with warm acceptance. The patient may just as frequently counter the therapist's efforts with condescending jibes and contemptuous ridicule. He may deprecate the humor and derogate the therapist's intelligence and skill by insisting that "making light of serious matters" displays an immature mind. A defensive therapist may become annoyed or hurt, but the patient's reaction can be seen as further evidence of the patient's intense seriousness and inability to touch lightly on many matters which are not actually crucial to his existence.

It is a laboratory demonstration of how the patient does react to attempts to make life more fun.

THE THERAPIST

While it is generally agreed that the sex of the therapist is not a significant factor in the therapy of obsessionals, the age, experience, and background are quite relevant—and at times very significant. One factor is crucial: the therapist must not be too obsessional himself, or he will inevitably get caught in a *folie à deux* which can prolong therapy indefinitely—if it manages to survive at all. This factor is undoubtedly one of the major issues that prolong therapy in these disorders, as well as does any tendency to be passive and thereby to encourage the patient's indecisiveness. A therapist who cannot get unlocked from the patient's struggles to control because he himself must always be in control either traps his patient into passive compliance and endless analysis or drives him away early by stirring up a great deal of hostility. Under such circumstances the patient and therapist may get into an obsessive bind in which the needs of each one may be satisfied at the high cost of permanent invalidism of the patient.

While the obsessional patient will prefer a therapist who is older and very experienced, he will often end up with the opposite, a younger and less experienced therapist who is less of a threat to his omniscience and thought to be more likely to be controlled and subdued.

To proceed successfully with the therapy of the obsessional, the therapist must be active, directive, and closely tuned to irrelevant communications in order that they can be turned off as quickly as possible. How can the therapist know what is relevant and what is irrelevant? Except in the extremes, this is a difficult and complicated problem. The recipe for a cake, or the number of cracks in the office ceiling, or the detailed description of occupational tasks can readily be identified as irrelevant to the therapeutic task at hand. The preoccupation with endless detail about one's early years, the school buildings, teachers, and empty accounts of earlier events may seem relevant, but may well turn out to be evasive devices to forestall the examination of one's feelings and attitudes toward the teacher or others. One might say, "That is very interesting, but what happened between you and the teacher?" We now know enough about personality development and certain characterological disorders to be sure that certain matters are entirely irrelevant, others are relevant, and most are open to question. It is in this in-between area that the skill, intuition, and experience of the therapist are called upon in order to make judgments about the relevance of the communication.

The relevance of certain communications will, of course, be determined by the particular theoretical predelictions of the therapist. Some therapists consider all communication about the patient's earlier years as relevant, while others feel that such a focus is not always useful. Some insist that any reality concerns are out of place in analysis, considering useful only data that concern the transference. There are wide differences in viewpoints, depending upon the therapist's theoretical position. However, it is universally agreed that the encouragement of certain details or topics tends to convey to the patient that some matters are of greater interest to the therapist, and this encourages their presentation.

Whatever the theoretical preference, certain issues are clearly irrelevant when they fail to advance the understanding of either the origin or the development of the personality defenses which characterize the disorder. Therefore, what is clearly relevant in all theoretical persuasions is material that touches on the dynamics of the obsessional state and the defense tactics which are an intrinsic part of it. Material which relates to anxieties (past or present), attempts at control, and preoccupations with guarantees and certainty, etc., are always pertinent and need to be encouraged. The patient's evasive and defensive tactics must be brought into the open.

Material with emotional content usually has some degree of relevance in the therapeutic situation. However, the difficulty in deciding what is relevant should not allow the therapist to encourage undirected free association which, in the obsessional, has a tendency to veer away from pertinent data. Neither should the notion that "everything is relevant" permit the therapist to allow treatment to continue endlessly because he is unwilling to narrow down the patient's communications. In a sense, everything can be shown to have a degree or relevance to everything else. However, it is no longer necessary to allow every therapeutic involvement to become a research project designed to prove the notions of determinism, unconscious motivation, etc. Therapy is a practical contract directed at illuminating and alleviating behavioral disorders. Increasing knowledge of these disorders has enabled us to localize our inquiries, thereby giving us some clues as to what is pertinent and what is not. What may appear relevant during one session may be irrelevant at another. It is a judgment which can only be made in terms of material to be dealt with at a particular time; it must be decided upon in a specific situation.

In discouraging certain communications at particular times, however, one must be careful not to discourage it altogether. When the obsessive recital of dreams may, at one time, be avoiding currently unpleasant issues, this avoidance needs to be made known. Yet it should not be done in a way that would be entirely discouraging.

As suggested above, the obsessional has a great capacity to confuse the therapeutic process by producing irrelevant free associations or by constantly changing the subject or by having a sticky inability to change the subject. Great skill is called for on the part of the therapist to direct or control these tendencies. The therapist must be able to intervene actively and draw the focus of attention back to the significant matters. The defensive maneuvers may require frequent and repeated attention.

The therapist must always be aware of the limits of his patient's capacities to tolerate certain interpretations or observations; he must stop short lest he increase the anxiety and the defenses which ordinarily protect the patient against anxiety. This will limit the patient's capacities to observe and acknowledge the therapist's interpretations. When interpretations are seen as criticisms or as deflating to the patient's esteem, the patient will react with even more elaborate defenses. On the other hand the therapist's observations must not be too bland or they may be easily overlooked.

Activity on the part of the therapist is an absolute essential from the beginning of the therapy to the end. Even a meagre understanding of the dynamics of the obsessional state requires that the therapist not permit the techniques which defeat communication to continue for too long a time—although the therapist's activities must never be so intense as to overwhelm the patient or make him feel that the therapy is being run by the therapist. It does mean that the therapist must understand the obsessional's defense mechanisms of maintaining anxiety at a minimum in order to facilitate learning and ultimately to resolve the obsessional patterns. Consequently, free association as well as the tendency to endless detail and circumstantiality in the obsessive accounts must be controlled by the therapist. Passivity in the therapist can only lead to interminable analyses in an atmosphere that becomes more clouded and confused, which is often the reason for the long, fruitless analyses which characterized an early stage in the development of the methodology of psychoanalytic treatment of the obsessional.

TRANSFERENCE AND
COUNTER-TRANSFERENCE

The therapist is universally viewed as an authoritative figure who expects and demands maximum and perfect behavior. The patient feels that these demands are unreasonable and irrational, and that the demands are more than he is capable of. The therapist clearly represents one parental figure who is more striking than the other and with whom there had been a relationship of some perverseness in terms of exaggerated expectations from the patient (which the patient felt to be far beyond his capacities). Often, both parents may be involved.

The therapist is seen as a critical, judging individual, with no respect for human frailties, who is sitting in judgment on every action of the patient. He is viewed as an unfriendly antagonist who must be overcome and exposed. At the same time, however, he must be impressed with the patient's skill and talents. It is only comparatively late in therapy that the patient can experience a collaborative interest on the part of the therapist and see him as a friendly helper rather than a caustic critic. Until then there is an ever-present atmosphere of suspicious uncertainty on the part of the patient and a readiness to hostility which is generally well disguised in a superficially friendly and respectful demeanor. Such an atmosphere is easily punctured at the slightest rise of tension. This often makes the patient uneasy, so that he will strive to undo any damage that might have resulted from his anger and irritation. He tends to attribute every deficiency which he despises in himself to the therapist. His charges will range from his feeling that the therapist is a perfectionist, a procrastinator, and an indecisive person to ideas that he is a hypocrite and phoney whose standards are so flexible that they lack integrity. One can get a very clear view as to what ails the patient by examining his distorted views of the therapist.

Generally, the traits and attitudes attributed to the therapist are largely irrational and unjustified, but some of the characterizations may be more or less true. The therapeutic atmosphere may very well be one of an irrational authority who expects the rules to be followed simply because they exist and who demands certain behavior because it is good for the patient. The silent, passive, unseen therapist can easily exaggerate the authoritative atmosphere of the therapeutic setting and unnecessarily aggravate or rationally confirm the patient's defenses. Some of the elements of the classical techniques tended to do this very thing. The patient was put in an inferior, reclining role and was forced, by the rules of the game, to take over and proceed with the job. He received few, if any, answers to questions that might disturb him, and he was faced with a totally unreal situation in which he either accepted the rules or left. Because of the severe discomforts of the obsessional way of life, he frequently decided to take the rules and fit them into his obsessional bundle of tricks. So therapy became another ritual rather than an experience in undoing his ritualistic symptoms. By following the rules rigidly and precisely and cooperating with every requirement of the process, the patient often reinforced his neurosis—which produced insuperable obstacles to its clarification and resolution. This frequently resulted in the patient's achieving considerable insight but failing to gain any change in behavior or charatcer structure as a result of the insight.

The therapist must be constantly aware that the obsessional's skill in deceiving himself and others and his secret demands for perfection, omniscience, and omnipotence reflect themselves in the relationship with him. Patients' apparent cordiality and conviviality in the face of an exchange in which they feel derogated must always be scrutinized, especially when the therapist is forced to make explanations or defenses of his interpretations. The cordiality is a thin veneer, and the underlying irritation and resentment must be brought into the open.

The counter-transference phenomenon, or the reaction of the therapist to the patient, will vary considerably from therapist to therapist. The responses of the therapist, however, are of invaluable significance in the elucidation of the obsessional's way of life. The increased utilization of the counter-transference phenomenon is one of the contributions of the post-Freudian psychoanalysts (this has been dealt with at length in the author's earlier book, *Developments in Psychoanalysis*).

The need for the therapist constantly to examine and occasionally to comment on his own feelings in response to some communication or the patient's behavior can bring the whole matter of emotions into the forefront of the work. The therapist may have some reaction to the patient's characteristic obsessional devices which can be identified, or to some covert process in which the therapist has unwittingly been drawn into a defensive role. In the latter situation he may feel particularly irritated at his own failure to be observant, a feeling which could be brought into the sessions. The way the therapist uses his reactions can be of great influence in the outcome of therapy. When he can be uninvolved in the sense of observing the patient's characteristic behavioral traits and identifying them, he can help the patient see what effect such behavior might have on others. At such times, the observations should be descriptive rather than critical and should convey good will and warm interest. On the other hand, when the patient's behavior is irritating and particularly annoying or puts the therapist in a bind and stimulates his own anxieties about his deficiencies, the therapist's open responses will not be useful to the patient unless the therapist can acknowledge his own limitations and show the patient how he succeeded in drawing the therapist into his own neurotic net. In such an instance the therapist must be prepared to acknowledge his own defensive needs and his own tendency to justify himself and to be correct. He must also be able to express irritation and annoyance at the patient's undercover derogating and deriding activities.

To be useful to the patient, such a procedure must be done in an atmosphere in which the emphasis is on the therapist's limitations and humanness, rather than on the patient's hostilities. The tendency to focus on the hostile behavior of the patient serves only to distract the therapeutic process from its real task of investigating the sources of the patient's uncertainties and his need for guarantees in living. The therapist can always turn the discussion onto these matters when the patient is hostile by expressing some curiosity about what the patient feels is being endangered that requires this hostile attack. In this way the hostility is seen only as a defense and not as a cause. It takes the focus off the hostility issue.

The therapist can use his reactions to initiate and accelerate insights by pointing out how the patient's behavior seems phoney, hypocritical, or grandiose. Again, this must be presented as an observation rather than a personal grievance or criticism. This can be done by wondering out loud whether others might not react in a similar way in response to many aspects of the patient's behavior. The use of a sharp or caustic comment, or the single, well-intoned phrase can often simulate greater emotional response than the well-phrased intellectual formulation, which usually stirs up a defensive counterattack. The emphasis must be on a comment which will stir up feelings without humiliating the patient. The production of humiliation will sidetrack the inquiry. Sullivan employed his reactions with great skill in his work with obsessionals, and this undoubtedly accounted for much of his success with them.

The need for the active participation of the therapist has already been stressed. It must be emphasized that the possibility of involvement, exchange, and participation of the therapist can stimulate the patient to commit himself and make known his real feelings and attitudes. It can supply the needed experience in risking a relationship with a figure who will not be punitive or rejecting. The more involved the patient gets in the therapy, the clearer will his subtle and most closely guarded techniques come out into the open and be available for study. The more gross and obvious techniques will become evident early in therapy and will make it possible for changes to be made. However, the more elusive and intricate neurotic patterns which closely resemble non-neurotic behavior can become clear only in the intricacies of a relationship in which the patient allows himself some freedom to relax and "let go." The best setting for such discoveries lies in the reactions of the therapist—usually called counter-transference feelings—to the patient's behavior. The training of the therapist permits him to recognize these maneuvers and to bring them to the patient's attention, thus helping the patient to eliminate them from his living.

One must clearly distinguish between becoming truly involved and getting into arguments in order to win. Getting entangled in the flypaper tactics of the obsessional is not necessarily becoming more intimate or more involved. Any involvements or interactions of the patient and therapist should always be with regard to the therapeutic task. While quarrelling indicates some involvement, it has no real place in the therapeutic process. The therapist must be aware that when he becomes active, certain safeguards must be applied so that activity does not turn into a repetition of the malevolent, authoritarian relationship which the patient had to deal with through his early experiencing. The interaction characterized by the "one-up-manship" maneuver to maintain control of the therapeutic work can illustrate dramatically some of the pitfalls of an unaware or unsophisticated therapist. What is designed as a collaborative adventure can be changed into a struggle for control and position, and the therapeutic process can be viewed by some as a state of warfare. While it may be a struggle, it is not a war; the goal is not to win a battle but to communicate meaning and understanding to another in order to help him deal with his problems in living.

If the therapist is unable to identify the patient's tactics of using double binds, semantic paradoxes, and verbal assaults—all devices used by obsessionals—therapy can very well develop into a state of war. The therapist must not lose sight of the fact that his job is to expose the tactics, not to beat the patient at his own game. Double binds are common occurrences in the obsessional's developmental history and in his own functioning, and one can easily be caught up in the "game" if one is not constantly on guard.

PAST VERSUS FUTURE

The obsessional is oriented toward the future in order to guarantee that his living be free of anxiety. Therefore, his interest in the past is generally meager, if not absent. At best, his recollection of his early years is distorted, and the stage is frequently seen as a time when he was mistreated by one or both parents in a hypercritical and demanding fashion. His recollections of the more recent past are generally seen as a succession of occasions when he was taken advantage of, pushed around, or was the object of discrimination by disrespectful people.

It was the obsessional's tendency to distort the past which produced the crisis in Freud's theorizing that ultimately resulted in his greatest discovery. On the basis of the accounts of his obsessional patients—who described passive sexual assaults in their early years—Freud postulated that the obsessive disorder was caused by such sexual assaults. When, however, he attempted to validate these accounts, he discovered that they were untrue and were fantasies of the patient. He was then forced to acknowledge that either his theories were based on lies, or he needed to explain such fantasized accounts in other ways. Freud resolved this difficulty when he recognized the power and significance of the imagination and the effect that thinking has on an individual's behavior. It became clear not only that actual events could produce widespread consequences but also that the person's imaginings or fantasies were capable of influencing his psychological history and behavior. Thus the recollections of an individual may not be a major concern, as they are very likely to be distorted. The obsessional's ability to reconstruct his early years is quite limited as he has little interest in the past. His present behavior is related not only to his past experiences but also to the variety of defenses erected in the early years. The obsessional may have learned very little from his past experiences because his defenses prevented him from drawing any reasonable deductions from them. Thus a successful experience or performance does not prevent anxiety about the next occasion. He approaches it with the same uneasiness and uncertainties, as though it had never happened before. Each occasion is a new trial in which he must prove himself over and over again.

Psychoanalytic therapy originally emphasized the need for a genetic reconstruction of the person's life, with emphasis on his libidinal development. It was assumed that the reconstructions would undo the repressions, which were the basis of the neurotic symptoms. However, much of the research on the therapeutic process and the ego psychological theories of personality development have raised doubts about the validity of this view. Whichever view may be correct, the possibility of an adequate or accurate genetic reconstruction of an obsessional's early life is highly questionable. Therefore, an emphasis on the past and the problem of the obsessional's distorted recollections makes the usefulness of this aspect of therapy highly uncertain.

The most effective approach seems to be in the examination of recent events—particularly those events that occur in the ongoing relationship with the therapist. In this sense the transference and counter-transference phenomena play their unique roles in advancing the therapeutic process. The emphasis on the "here and now" by many post-Freudian theorists finds its greatest reward in the treatment of obsessional disorders. The more recent conceptions of mental illness do not focus exclusively on the genesis of these disorders as libidinal deformations, nor do they conceive of the beginnings in relation to any specific trauma. The developments are seen as occurring in an atmosphere in which repeated experiences produce effects on the person in obvious or subtle ways. Therefore, discovering the actual origin or beginning of a symptom or personality characteristic seems of less value than a general recognition of the milieu or atmosphere of the household, or the general attitudes of the parents. In the ultimate development of the behavioral disorder, the conditioning effect of repeated experiences plays a major role, in addition to that of the initiating cause. In the adult years one deals with a problem the origin of which is only a single element in its continuation; the persistence of the faulty pattern is related to the process of conditioning and habit. Therapy must unravel the detailed and widespread defensive techniques which develop and penetrate into every aspect of the obsessional's life, as well as search for the origins of the symptoms. This requires a knowledge of the patient's present living in order that the therapist may see the subtleties and intricacies of his defensive processes. This is a most difficult task and comprises the bulk of the work in the therapeutic process. To achieve this the therapist must be prepared for a long and arduous job of repeating the same observations and interpretations frequently before they are truly recognized by the patient. It requires patience and understanding of the tenacious and persistent nature of the obsessional process.

One may find that the patient avoids present failures or recognized deficiencies as they tend to expose too much of his feelings. In contrast, past angers can be described and experienced calmly, so that the actual value of their assessment in the therapeutic process is sharply reduced. Present emotional responses must be faced, and, as they are impinging on other responses, they can be usefully explored. As the exploration of such emotional experience is crucial to any useful work, stress on the here-and-now serves this purpose very well.

PROBLEMS OF CONTROL

Therapy requires a free, uncontrolling attitude toward one's thoughts, and the ability to say aloud whatever may come to mind. Ordinarily, the obsessional tries to examine, appraise, and "screen" every thought before he utters it in order to avoid exposing himself unfavorably. Thus on the one hand his impulse is to censor anything that might make him appear in an unflattering light, while on the other hand he has a need to follow the therapist's instruction meticulously. In trying to do the latter he gets hung-up on endless, detailed elaborations of each thought that may unwittingly expose too much. The free flow of associations is also impeded by his difficulty in getting off a subject once it is started, thereby dwelling on what is no longer associative data but merely detailed bits of data. Any idea, thought, or attitude that happens to come to mind is simply worked to death. Both of these tendencies may succeed in controlling the content of the psychoanalytic hour.

The patient may frequently bring a written or memorized agenda to the session, which is intended to rigidly control the content of the session and guarantee that nothing is left out—and that nothing is inadvertently added. Fringe thoughts or ideas which occur in the course of the session are generally not permitted to interrupt or alter the prearranged presentation. The patient may unconsciously select and censor his thoughts in order to control the content of the interview. This must be brought to his attention—not as an aspect of his deceitfulness or failure to cooperate, but as an impediment in the therapeutic process.

A patient who early in his therapy manifested overt and covert tendencies to try to run the therapeutic sessions by having an unwritten agenda wanted to take over the role of therapist. On one occasion, while this patient was deciding what was relevant to discuss, I pointed out that this was his method of controlling the sessions and that it would be preferable if he did not decide for himself unless the matter concerned something unquestionably irrelevant. He agreed and then went to the other extreme. He stated that he would therefore make no judgments of relevance at all; he wanted me to make the decision so that he would not be accused of censoring any material. However, this could allow *him* to criticize or discount any judgments I might make. He was in effect saying, "Fine. I'll do what you say but I'm letting you know now that unless I run the show, I'll criticize it, or else take no responsibility for the consequences."

While insisting that he should not be asked to decide about the relevance of certain matters until he was much better informed, he still tried to run the process. I was trying to say that he should not control the process, but he was attempting to control it more effectively.

The tendency of some patients to stay rigidly on a topic and avoid fringe thoughts or associations might seem to indicate their efforts to avoid distraction. While this may be the case, it is also a way of avoiding unplanned or spontaneous reactions. That is, as one cannot predict the consequences of such reactions it is safer not to evoke them at all.

The problem of an agenda and the rigid adherence to a plan was exemplified in the behavior of an obsessional who became preoccupied prior to each session with concerns about *not* bringing an agenda to insure that he would freely present whatever came to mind. This was particularly true with regard to his concerns about his grandiose fantasies. If he were consciously concerned about some important matter, then he could *not* bring it up as this would be preplanning. Therefore, important material would be postponed for long periods of time until it would be accidentally revealed.

Control of a situation can be direct or indirect, subtle and unwitting, or calculated and obvious. The controlling tactics used by an obsessional, however, are rarely obvious to him, even though they may seem blatant and unmistakable to others. One image the obsessional has of himself is of someone who is under the influence of others, pushed and pulled by them. He sees himself a passive victim of the demands and requirements of others and he feels himself to be helpless in the face of forces he must overcome. While he may see his helplessness, he generally does not recognize his defensive, controlling tactics, and the striving for power involved in them. These elements must be drawn to his attention in the therapeutic process. To become aware of how he appears to others can help him understand why others react to him as they generally do.

One of the most effective techniques for controlling others is to put oneself entirely at the other's disposal and to abandon all pretense and plans for directing one's own life. While this appears to be a state of total dependency and can result in rejection, it may succeed in getting the other person to focus entirely on fulfilling the obsessional's needs. The risk of failure is present, but it is fairly safe to assume that in a middle-class Western culture such a display of total incapacity will stir up sympathy and help rather than open rejection. While it may overtly convey a total lack of control of the universe, covertly it serves to manipulate others through the emotional influence of helplessness. This type of "no control" is often a most effective device for exerting maximum control over others.

This personality trait manifests itself in the seemingly self-effacing, compliant person who presumes to do exactly what you want him to. He follows all rules and procedures precisely. In therapy he will free-associate and will not withhold anything, following all instructions scrupulously. He will say anything and everything that comes to mind, incuding stock quotations, the number of cracks in the ceiling, the voluminous details of an exchange with the florist about how to care for African violets, and every last detail—inning by inning—of the baseball game.

The overconforming literalness of this type of response tends to sabotage and interfere with the therapeutic process because it wastes so much time on what is clearly irrelevant and serves to distract from the relevant. When this is called to the patient's attention he may respond with: "You told me to say everything that comes to my mind and not to censor any of it." In fact, these are the instructions he received. He is afraid not to say everything lest he leave out something important. If anything might be significant, then his devotion to the total truth as well as his rigidity about the rules justify such detail.

The therapist must therefore be alert to who is controlling the interview and the therapy. It must always be very clear as to who is the doctor and who is the patient.

TUG-OF-WAR

In his relationships the obsessional invariably becomes involved in a tug-of-war when he attempts to "one-up" others, both in therapy and out. Since his security rests upon his always being right, even the most trivial exchange becomes a duel which he must win. In therapy he may have to have the last word, with a routine question or comment—even if it may undo the whole hour's work or may cast doubt upon the entire exchange. At another time he may challenge the therapist's capability in an attempt to put him on the defensive. This puts the therapist in an inferior role and requires him to explain his actions to another person who sits in judgment upon him. This technique is used in other personality configurations as well, but it is particularly common in obsessional relationships.

In the tug-of-war the patient tries to gain control by raising doubts about the validity of the process, the theory which underlies it, or the capacity of the therapist to utilize both. The patient not only may raise doubts about the matter of the unconscious or the validity of the introspection but also may begin to attack psychotherapy as a pseudo-science and the practitioners as dupes or quacks. These attacks are generally timed to deal with the patient's feelings that the therapeutic situation is a hostile one and the therapist is criticizing him and putting him in his place. He feels that he must counterattack and reassert his position. It is important that at such times the therapist does not get caught up with the patient's hostility and view it as if it were the primary issue. The patient is trying to establish some parity in a situation in which he feels himself to be inferior, and his hostility is a defensive device to overcome this supposed inferiority.

Hostile and aggressive feelings are often responsible for a great many of the obsessional's difficulties. However, the need to establish parity or even superiority may or may not involve feelings of hostility toward others. If his sense of control is endangered, as in a therapeutic situation in which he is forced to recognize his fallibility, the patient may very well react with anger and irritation and attack the therapist. The basis for such an attack can be clearly understood in terms of a need to control rather than as reflecting some underlying "hostile core." The patient has great concerns about controlling his hostile impulses, as well as everything else, and it is therefore necessary to understand the causes of his hostility. In spite of the prevalence of hostile feelings in the obsessional, he has more difficulty in dealing with his tender impulses and his fear that they may get out of control and that he might be overly kind or loving. These reactions are even more dangerous than his hostile feelings, because he sees them as weak, as giving up, and as losing the tug-of-war. Being tender means being a sucker or being taken advantage of; this feeling is untenable for him.

The struggle to be on top in the therapeutic situation may extend over long periods of time. Occasionally, it can be resolved early in therapy, but because it reflects the totality of the obsessional's character structure it generally weaves in and out of the therapeutic process from beginning to end.

A patient spent several weeks exploring his objections to a statement I made, and finally appeared with evidence to prove that I was wrong. He had difficulty understanding that I might have accepted his objections at the time I made the statement and that he need not have spent so much time researching his challenge. He felt I would defend my statement to the death, just as he would have; therefore he needed support for his attack. In the interval, while he was accumulating data to counter my statement, he was subtly contemptuous of me, buoyed up by the knowledge that he had won the argument.

A comfortable capacity to admit errors and fallibility without any pretense of humility or virtue is an important quality in the therapist—not only to avoid the tug-of-war but also to demonstrate the possibility that one can be wrong and survive without humiliation or anguish. There are many such opportunities in the course of therapy and the therapist should not pass up any occasion to admit his error when he turns out to be wrong. *Staging* such an event in order to give the patient such an experience may create an atmosphere of trickery with regard to the therapist as well as the process as a whole. One can be sure that enough situations will occur spontaneously so that the therapist need not search for such opportunities.

It is obvious that the therapist cannot enter into the tug-of-war in order to overcome his "opponent." There are more significant issues involved which concern the elucidation and demonstration of the patient's insistent need to win or be on top. He must be helped to see how this interferes with learning and relating effectively with people. To win in an immediate sense may often mean gaining control, but such control can be useless and ineffective. The tug-of-war, when it occurs in therapy, provides an opportunity for the obsessional patient to see in microscopic proportions how he functions in the world at large. Winning, which may supercede all other values for him, can be more costly than it is worth. Therefore, the tug-of-war is a most effective therapeutic tool if the therapist can use it skillfully. He should not avoid a challenge on the assumption that the patient may convert it into a battle, but should grasp the chance to enlighten the patient about this tendency. If the therapist evades the challenge, he encourages the grandiose fantasies of the patient and strengthens his neurotic defenses. Intelligent confrontation and involvement—in which the therapist stands firm while yielding at opportune moments—can provide great enlightenment to the patient.

PROBLEMS OF PERFECTION

The desire to be perfect leads to a variety of complications in the therapeutic process, as therapy is basically a learning situation and the obsessive is unable to admit to deficiencies in his living. His security rests upon a presumed invulnerability based on his feelings of perfection and omniscience. He has the illusion that he can meet any challenge and can therefore be certain about his existence. An interpretation or observation which is unexpected, unfamiliar, or novel, and which might challenge this conviction, is either denied, repressed, or overlooked. If it cannot be by-passed in these ways it is either minimized or rationalized as reflecting the therapist's jealousy or critical unfriendliness. At these times the patient views therapy as a battle; he feels he must defend himself against attack. This will occur in spite of his awareness of the need for therapy. He may even be aware of his unreasonable tendency to react as though attacked, yet he must still defend himself to maintain his illusion of perfection.

Such contradictory behavior is comprehensible when one recognizes that the obsessional's neurotic integration rests on the need to deny any deficiency or lack of knowledge about himself and the universe. Therefore he must resist or parry every observation which reflects on this matter. He may produce new data to cast doubt on the truth of any such observation made by the therapist. He will raise insignificant exceptions to question the validity of the interpretation. If the therapist's interpretation is convincing and cannot be evaded, the patient minimizes its value in order to make it more palatable and to reduce the shame of having to admit that he did not already know about the matter, Although he may accept the interpretation, he will move on quickly to other matters which, he says, are more important. Thus the impact is reduced. At other times, while ostensibly agreeing with the interpretation, he will set up a barrage of highly intellectualized counterattacks to undermine or undo the interpretation.

After many qualifications and clarifications he may finally accept the interpretation—but not without some belligerent counterattack. He may charge the therapist with running him down or with trying to destroy his self-esteem. Such an attack may put the therapist on the defensive and serve to tone down the interpretation, so that the real issue is evaded.

The patient may, at times, deny the observation only to discover it himself as a fresh and novel idea in succeeding hours. He will behave as if he figured it out all alone and will present it as a fascinating discovery. In doing this he can salvage the notion of his perfection and maintain the fiction of his flexibility. The patient's need to be perfect pushes him to present the most precise and extensive account of every event to be certain that nothing is left out. This produces an enumeration of the most minute details and accounts of minor and insignificant events. He will ramble on endlessly in his need to clarify and qualify every statement. Such endless detail may be rationalized as accurate reporting.

One gets a clear impression, however, that the patient has no capacity to separate the relevant from the irrelevant. While this type of communication outside of therapy may be only boring and irritating, it is most important that in therapy the patient note the effect of such tendencies.

The patient attempts to retain the illusion of perfection by being doubtful or inattentive to interpretations. Since interpretations are the only way to advance a real understanding of the obsessional defenses, the patient's tendency to maintain his neurotic esteem and avoid what he considers to be a humiliating acceptance of shortcomings may prevent any movement in therapy. The undoing process often occurs even while the therapist is speaking. As he listens, the patient is already preparing his defenses, justifications, or counterattacks and is thus only partly paying attention to the therapist's statement. He may even feel superior by deciding that the interpretation does not go far enough and that the therapist is not so bright after all. Some patients literally hear nothing of what is said. They may often be able to identify exactly when they stopped hearing and began ruminating about some irrelevancy unconnected with the immediate exchange. This must be dealt with summarily, or valid and valuable exchanges can take place without any noticeable effect on the patient. The most brilliant observations or formulations can be wasted unless they are attended to; this requires that the therapist present them in a palatable fashion. The therapist's skill is manifested most clearly in his capacity to deal with this particular problem.

The emphasis on intellectuality is another means of avoiding the potential humiliation of not being perfect. It prevents real involvements in any emotional exchange and thereby sidetracks the possibility of being influenced or affected by the therapist's interpretation or observation. Intellectualizing and philosophizing about life is a most successful device to avoid participating in it. The obsessional exhibits great skill in avoiding any involvement with the therapist, although he may talk extensively about involvement and the problems of transference and counter-transference. He will even talk about feelings and emotions. However, it will be a succession of words drawn from an intellectual comprehension of the issues involved, devoid of any real emotional response. It is therefore necessary to focus on real feelings and to limit, as much as possible, such intellectual discussions. Obviously, they cannot be avoided entirely, but they can and should be minimized and, whenever possible, their true function demonstrated to the patient.

An aspect of perfection which poses innumerable therapeutic problems is the obsessional's tendency to think and live in extremes. For him, it is not a matter of being correct, but of being perfect. His living is secure only when he can be assured of absolute safety, infallible prediction, and absolute certainty about his status—absolutes demanding superhuman attributes. The reaction to any discovery of inadequacy in therapy is one of *extreme* despair, discouragement, and feeling of failure.

Any attempt, therefore, to highlight these extreme demands in therapy and to portray the impossibility of fulfilling them may result in a counter-charge that the therapist is supporting the opposite extreme and is trying to make the patient into an ordinary or mediocre person. Each time the therapist tries to point out that the demands for perfection are unachievable and only lead to despair and disappointment he may be accused of having standards which are too low and of being too easily satisfied. At the beginning of therapy it is impossible for the patient to take a middle ground, i.e., to do the best he can or to utilize the skills which he does have. He insists that this is not enough. As long as he must have absolute guarantees he cannot be satisfied with human uncertainties. He cannot see that to accept one's human limitations is an act of *strength* that accounts for some of man's great achievements. The need to reassert this constantly in the therapeutic exchanges results in the charge that therapy is attempting to reduce the patient's performance to a minimum. It is hard for the patient to accept the fact that being human does not mean being satisfied with the least output, or the utilization of only a fraction of one's capacities. The therapist must regularly interpret and demonstrate that the insistence on perfection produces the very results the patient abhors. Mediocrity is *not* the alternative to the superhuman expectations of the obsessional, although this is the only way he can see it. He sees the world in extremes because he lives that way and feels that unless he is pushed to act he will not perform at all. Therefore, when he is encouraged to relax or to limit his demands, he interprets this as encouragement to slacken his standards.

The therapist must help the obsessional patient to recognize that doing the best one is capable of is neither mediocre nor ordinary, but richly productive. To help the patient strive for a realizeable goal which utilizes his highest skills and capacities is not a matter of compromise. One is not either a God or a shameful mortal. One can be proud and productive even while restrained by human limitations.

If security is attainable only by being King then one cannot accept the role of Prime Minister, which is just as unsafe as being an ordinary citizen. This is the essence of the problem of extremes in the obsessional, and no amount of reassurance about the value of being second best will suffice. Since the excessive demands owe to compulsive requirements, an intellectual clarification of the problem does not serve to reduce it even though it paves the way for eventual change.

The dilemma of the extremes and the contradictory behavior resulting from them is reflected in the obsessional's inconsistent attitudes toward his need for others and his need to present himself as entirely independent and self-sufficient. The contradiction between his dependent and independent needs creates innumerable therapeutic crises and impasses which need to be clarified by frequent interpretation and repetition. This is particularly highlighted in the phobic states when the obsessional requires the presence of another person in order to function at all. Although he insists upon total independence, his phobia requires and therefore justifies his dependence. Independent and self-reliant behavior is preferred by the obsessional as it helps sustain the illusion of a perfect, infallible, omniscient being. Total independence, however, cannot be achieved; the obsessional is forced to rely upon others—to marry, to go to a doctor, etc. This reflects itself in the therapeutic process when the obsessional grudgingly admits that he is in need of treatment or insists that he is doing it for someone else. By going to a psychotherapist he is satisfying someone else's needs. He frequently reminds the therapist that while the therapy may be useful, it is not really necessary for him. But, he adds, since he is in treatment, why has it not overcome all the problems which he refuses to admit he had in the first place?

Whatever his reasons for being in therapy, what he really wants from therapy, on one level, is to become more perfect and to overcome the deficiencies which interfere with his achieving perfection. Being forced to acknowledge his deficiencies because of some crisis or unfortunate circumstance, he expects that therapy will now overcome them and make him totally independent. However, he wants the therapy and the therapist to accomplish this. He is willing to acknowledge the expertness of the psychiatrist, to pay his fees, and to follow all the necessary instructions. In return, he expects the doctor to resolve the difficulties. The concepts of relationship, mutual endeavor, and collaboration, are alien to him. As he doesn't really feel that he needs the therapist, he has no need to develop any relationship with him.

The obsessional is particularly incompetent in the area of interpersonal relationship. Relationship involves participation which, in turn, implies some need or dependency as well as commitment and exchange that grows out of some trust in the relationship. The demand for self-sufficiency obviates and complicates all his attempts at forming relationships, and this becomes more aggravated as he grows older. Intimacy, either sexual or nonsexual, is largely foreign to him because he has had such limited experience with it. Yet nonsexual intimacy is what the therapeutic relationship requires.

To help the obsessional gain insight into how he actually behaves, requires not only the clear recollection of a recent event but also the elimination of the patient's doubts and uncertainties about such events. The "here and now" experience allows the therapist to pin down the facts of an event and the patient's feelings about it. His reaction to an event and his way of dealing with his anxieties are more easily ascertained when one explores a recent event that is uncluttered by the distortions, denials, or sheer forgetting permitted by the passage of time. For the obsessional, past events and hazy recollections are ideal opportunities to use powers of verbal manipulation and distortion. The patient finds it easier to restrict his communication to the past. It is easier for him to discuss angers, frustrations, or difficulties that occurred years ago. Because the emotional elements in the obsessional's life are generally constrained and under control, it is imperative that they be brought into focus with regard to his present attitudes and relationships.

PROBLEMS OF OMNISCIENCE

If the patient expects to know everything, he feels utterly humiliated when he is forced to acknowledge a new piece of information. The obsessional must accept new insights and points of view about his past and present living, and he must come to recognize that his preconceptions and distortions restrict and prejudice his present experiences. He must learn that he is not viewing the environment with fresh and open eyes. He must see that he cannot really learn unless he is able to observe what is actually happening. He must learn to learn by becoming aware of his tendency to see everything in the light of what he expects to find in the first place. This is the "self-fulfilling prophecy" concept, which plays a vital role in all neurotic processes. When one expects or anticipates rejection, hostility, or criticism, one can misconstrue or misinterpret a situation in this light. An individual's uneasiness or anxiety may stimulate or produce an anxious situation which may then make the other participant uneasy; this reaction can then be interpreted as unfriendly, preventing the obsessional from discovering how the other person actually feels about him or whether the other person's reaction was a response to him or to other elements in the situation.

The inability to acknowledge limitations makes every observation, interpretation, or clarification a criticism and a challenge to the obsessional's omniscience. He cannot admit that there are things he does not know. He must challenge each observation at length, even while he may be aware that it is correct and useful. Most often, the patient's behavior is out of his awareness, and he automatically defends his position. His defensiveness may be manifested by his going on the offensive and saying that the interpretation is wrong or, if right, that it is too strong, poorly timed, and badly done because it came through as criticism and derogation rather than a simple observation. He is on the attack and tries to embarrass the therapist and put him on the defensive. His need to be critical has enabled him to develop his skills in finding the weak and vulnerable areas in his opponent. Such maneuvers not only tend to weaken the therapist's observations but also serve to shift the focus from the patient's deficiencies to the therapist's weaknesses.

To minimize the patient's resistances to learning, the therapist's interpretations should not be presented as if they were obvious. Instead, they should be presented as curious and interesting observations which the patient himself can elaborate upon. One should avoid saying, "From what you have said about the event, it is clear that your competitive need to excel must alienate others." Instead, it would be preferable to say, "What effect did you think your pushing John aside might have had upon him?" or "How would you react in the face of a competitor who was pressing hard to beat you?" One should pose interpretations in the form of "riddles" in which the necessary ingredients for a solution can be supplied by the patient. In this way the patient makes the discovery which leads to some useful interpretations and does not have to resist the information. While this works very effectively for awhile, the patient may soon catch on to the device and feel that it is an attempt to trick him. Even when discovered, it turns out to be more palatable than other techniques. As suggested above, the patient may at other times hear an interpretation, deny it, and return several weeks later to announce that he has just discovered it himself. One cannot force or hurry understanding in such patients; one needs to repeat, over and over again. To make it more likely that the interpretation will take hold, the therapist must hold it back until life's experiences are so clear and almost self-evident that the patient is ready to have such an insight himself. Above all, the interpretation must not be made in an attacking or critical vein, such as, "How come you didn't see it?" (implying "You must have been stupid not to notice it!"). Often a preliminary statement noting why it would have been difficult for the patient to recognize it sooner can make a strong interpretation more palatable. Yet no amount of skill and maneuver can make an interpretation easy for the obsessional to take. He has to discover that he does not know everything, and this stirs up much resentment.

Some obsessionals who are able to limit the range of their interests may become bright, well-informed, and highly proficient in their professional fields. Others, however, may have a superficial knowledge of many matters. Because they are aware of a lack of depth in many areas of knowledge they avoid detailed discussions and prefer to keep matters on a surface level. If challenged in discussions they make extreme and dogmatic statements in an effort to overwhelm their opponents and thereby terminate the discussion. Thus they frequently take extreme positions which are difficult to defend and they often find themselves supporting a point of view in which they do not believe. These complications generally arise when they are unwilling to admit to a lack of knowledge or an error and become entangled in a web of indefensible rationalizations.

This happens regularly in therapy when the obsessional faces someone who is better informed than he is on at least one subject. The therapist will have many opportunities to demonstrate such complications; because of their need to know everything, obsessionals will invariably "stick their necks out" and the consequences can be quite humiliating to them. The therapist must exert great care not to get involved to the point of humiliation, but to interrupt the patient before he goes too far. Past experiences, both inside and outside of therapy sessions, can be used to document the therapist's presentation instead of allowing the present situation to unfold completely. In this way the emotional encounter with the therapist can be used to advance the therapeutic process without stirring up too much resistance.

The patient may sometimes be eager to accept the therapist's observation and demonstrate his understanding, but he may leave no time for the amplification of the interpretation. He conveys the notion that he knew it all the time so "let's get on with it." He may, at times, even proceed to a statement about the therapist's great memory or his cleverness in understanding human behavior. This not only changes the focus of the exchange but also serves to stimulate the therapist's good will toward the patient. It is necessary on such occasions to examine this maneuver as well as the interpretation. The therapist must show the patient that his readiness to receive the interpretation was intended as flattery to the therapist as well as evidence of his own cleverness. The remark can then be seen as a maneuver in which the patient is actually shifting the focus from his behavior to the therapist's behavior.

In his omniscient strivings the patient may try to become informed about psychiatry in general and the therapist's professional orientation in particular. This fulfills the patient's need to know everything but also supplies him with ammunition to flatter or attack the therapist when a suitable occasion arises. As psychotherapy is still a young, growing science, it has many schisms and factions. Both organizationally and scientifically there are opposing points of view and, at times, bitter factional disputes. The patient may take advantage of this situation and adopt a superior attitude toward "petty, quarrelsome scientists who haven't been able to put their own house in order." On the other hand, he may become an active partisan or proselyte of his own therapist's persuasion.

As he becomes well-informed about the particular orientation of his therapist, the patient may color his observations and experiences, emphasizing those aspects which he assumes to be of interest to his therapist and minimizing others. He soon learns that his therapist is particularly interested in sex or dreams, or recent versus past experiences. He may unwittingly slant his presentation to suit these interests. While this occurs more or less in all patients, it is particularly so for the obsessional, who places great emphasis on intellectual skill and one-up-manship. In these situations, the omniscient strivings serve many purposes.

The emphasis on knowing also allows the patient to deal with the therapeutic process by the use of psychoanalytic jargon, which can result in an intellectual exercise that makes therapy an examination of psychoanalytic theory rather than of the patient's behavior. The patient attempts to deal with the therapist by impressing him with his brilliant observations—to be looked at in terms of theory rather than in terms of his own life. Too often the therapist himself is guilty of substituting psychoanalytic jargon for comprehensible language. The obsessional patient can become quite expert in using this terminology to enter the "club," but it serves to evade a meaningful confrontation with his attitudes and behavior. Freud had this type of person in mind when he advised his patients against reading or becoming too familiar with psychoanalytic literature. He wished to avoid as much as possible any slanting of a patient's productions which would be stimulated by reading. He also wanted to forestall discussions about psychoanalysis that might be stimulated by such reading. Although this injunction still remains useful, it has become impractical because most patients have already become acquainted with psychoanalytic writings either in popularized or professional form.

In the service of pleasing the therapist and fortifying his theories, a patient may avoid discoveries or observations which he thinks may negate these theories. In his own search for certainty and in his skill at accumulating knowledge the patient may not want to disturb the therapist's established systems. He needs to view the therapist as an idealized figure, in order to put his trust in him. To preserve this image the patient may forego criticism and intellectual disagreement. He may even seek out evidence or distort observations in order to fortify the therapist's analytic orientation. Such activity must be dealt with by the therapist with dispatch and in a forthright fashion if the therapy is not to become a technical course or a mutual admiration society.

If the therapist is himself obsessional, and requires such idealization, the therapeutic process reaches a stalemate. It may appear to be progressing well with few complications, but little therapeutic progress will be noted and therapy may become an interminable process.

PROBLEMS OF GRANDIOSITY

The obsessional's grandiosity is often manifested in his arrogant and contemptuous behavior, even though it may be dressed in a cloak of modesty and humbleness. He may expose his snobbishness and haughty behavior by slips of the tongue, accidental oversights, or deliberate deletions.

One patient, while standing in a cafeteria line with his wife, had ordered two rare roast beef sandwiches. One turned out to be less "rare" than the other. The patient insisted that the less rare one was his wife's. This resulted in a rather heated argument about the restaurant and its defects. After he related the story during a therapeutic session, I asked him how he knew that the less rare sandwich (the least desirable one), was his wife's, since he had picked them both off the counter. He sud-

denly became silent and was dumbfounded when he realized that
he had automatically taken it for granted that the "better" one
was naturally for him. It was also striking that his wife did not
make this observation but instead got into an argument about
the restaurant and the poor service. The patient operated under
the assumption that he was a privileged and special person whose
desires were to be catered to at all times.

To maintain the illusion of superiority and to protect his
grandiose conception of himself, the obsessional may limit his
socializing to inferiors or to occasions when his superior feelings
will go unchallenged. He may feel marked envy and anxiety in
the presence of realistic status differences, and while he may
yearn for relationships with higher-status individuals, he will
either derogate them or discover some deficiency in them that
allows him to eliminate them as potential friends. If they are
rich, they may not be intelligent enough. If they are intelligent,
he will insist that they are phony or pretentious. However,
resolving the dilemma by limiting his relationships to inferiors
leaves great areas of dissatisfaction because his own status is not
sufficiently acknowledged by associating with such people.

In therapy, grandiosity manifests itself in a variety of ways;
it needs to be identified whenever it appears. This issue often
accounts for the aloofness and the failure to become involved
in a relationship with the therapist. The patient remains distant
but proper, and does the job as it is outlined to him. Secretly,
he feels superior and contemptuous of the therapist; he is "on"
to what is happening. He feels smug and "above it all." He may
catalog the therapist's deficiencies—storing them for use at a
proper time. He may, for example, keep track of the time the
sessions start, watching to see that he gets all the time he is
entitled to, and store up evidence of the therapist's oversight.
Such stored-up grievances are usually held as secret weapons
and are revealed only under sufficient provocation. Meanwhile,
they may be used to maintain secret feelings of superiority in his
relationship to the therapist.

Such feelings may seriously interfere with the therapeutic

work, not only because they are secret, but because they are used to discount or discard any formulations which the patient doesn't like. They help the patient remain on the outside, looking in. By feeling superior to what is going on, the patient remains uninvolved while he is supposedly participating in a mutual exchange. If the therapist fails to bring this into the open, documenting it well, it will seriously hamper the progress of therapy. If the therapist succeeds in exposing this technique to the patient, it will enhance the patient's respect for the therapist.

In this connection, a patient related an incident concerning his pregnant wife, who awakened in the middle of the night with a cramp and proceeded to waken him. He became furious with her for awakening him—showing no concern about her pregnancy and suggesting that if she could not control her wakefulness she might sleep in another room. The following morning he recognized the arrogance of his attitude and felt quite remorseful. However, while relating the incident, he also reported his fantasy of how he thought I might behave under similar circumstances. In his fantasy he assumed that I allowed my wife to push me around and he felt contempt for me because of this. When I called attention to the difficulties he had in making his tenderness for his wife evident, he fantasized that I was a softie who couldn't stick up for my rights. He was certainly remorseful about what he could recognize as arrogant behavior toward his wife, but was unaware of his arrogance toward me during this exchange. I called his attention to this, and to how he felt toward me because he thought that I was taking his wife's side. He could then see his arrogance as it was expressed in various relationships.

The obsessional's grandiosity leads him to expect magical leaps and massive advances in therapy. He is impatient with small gains and expects every meaningful interpretation to be followed by great advances or total cure. There is often a profound disappointment when an illuminating exchange is followed by a repetition of the old pattern. When this happens, the patient criticizes the therapist and the psychotherapeutic theory as well as himself because he feels that he has failed to live up to his own grandiose expectations. As he can accept only total and complete restoration of his grandiose self through therapy, he cannot abide the slow, gradual process of learning and changing. This leads him to the frequent charge that the therapy is doing no good—"Nothing has changed"; "it's been a waste of time and money." The therapist must avoid trying to justify his work or blaming events on the patient's lack of cooperation. When progress is slow or absent, the therapist should not put the blame on the patient's resistance or resort to the concept of the negative therapeutic response. While many factors may be at work in the negative therapeutic reaction, it is clear that many therapeutic impasses or failures are also caused by the therapist's inadequate handling of the obsessional defense; this the therapist must face and take responsibility for. Therefore, failure cannot be said to be the fault of either the patient or therapist exclusively. However, understanding of undue expectation, a need for magical solutions, and feelings of despair and disappointment when immediate success is not forthcoming is of particular significance in the treatment of obsessionals.

The therapist must show interest in the patient's charges that the work is not going well or that little progress has been made. He should not act as though such charges are entirely unjustified and as if he were always above reproach. Generally, one can find both rational and irrational elements in a patient's complaints, and when dealt with seriously, they offer an opportunity for the patient to examine his grandiose expectations and for the therapist to explore his own deficiencies. An admission of the slowness of the process and the limited success it has produced presents the patient with a view of the therapist's realistic goals in contrast to the patient's extravagant expectations. It may even be useful for the patient to recognize that because of the comparatively youthful state of the science of psychotherapy, the therapist is bound by limitations imposed by the science itself. This is a valuable learning experience for someone whose major difficulty lies in his reluctance to acknowledge any limitations caused by nature or biology. To have this acknowledged in a matter-of-fact way, without apologies, may be of great help in getting the patient to accept some limitations in his own existence. Such an exchange may well serve to increase the patient's respect for the therapist's honesty and integrity.

The obsessional's hope that psychotherapy will enable him to become perfect and invulnerable is an aspect of his expectations which often overshadows all of his goals. He hopes that it will build up his resources so that he will never need to be dependent upon anyone, and that it will strengthen his esteem so that he will never again need to be beholden. He hopes therapy will provide him with sufficient placidity and detachment so that he need not be upset or distressed under any circumstances, even unfavorable ones. In short, he secretly hopes to repair his deficiencies and overcome his weaknesses and be made perfect—all as a result of therapy. When he discovers that, instead of making him a superman, therapy attempts to strengthen his humanness and get him to accept his imperfections, he is both angry and disappointed. Instead of an anxiety-free existence in a state of perfect living, he discovers that therapy will only help him to live with anxiety in an imperfect world in which he will have no ultimate control over his destiny. Such goals are so alien to him that he considers himself a failure for even approaching them. This produces the typical obsessional dilemma; as he becomes emotionally and psychologically more mature, he seems to feel that he is getting worse. However, as therapy progresses, he comes to realize that in the long run to accept his humanness will provide a more valid source of security. At this time, the patient's complaint that he is getting worse is often evidence of improvement—particularly when it is clear that getting worse means becoming less dependent upon his neurotic patterns. It is crucial that these factors be clearly explained to the patient, so that he can tolerate some temporary discomforts for the ultimate increase in his security.

CHAPTER 10

Clinical
Considerations

The process of change for the obsessional is
viewed as a potential source of danger
which may leave him vulnerable and uncertain; therefore he is
reluctant to put new insights into action. It is not surprising that
most of the obsessional's early attempts to move into new situations and relationships will be inclined to falter or fail. Since
he has little confidence in his capacity to fulfill his extravagant
expectations, he enters every new involvement with some apprehension and uneasiness. Thus his involvements are tentative and
uncertain, which prejudices the outcome in advance. He may
abandon his efforts too early because he cannot see the project's
being successful. If he continues the effort and completes it, he
may feel that the situation did not yield so rich a reward as
he expected from his new patterns of behavior. The new way
of operating initially has more anxiety than the old, familiar
way. Therefore the therapist must be prepared for complaints

and grievances about these experiments, which never come off to the full satisfaction of the patient.

One such patient could not hand in any reports at his job until he checked every reference twice and agonized over every grammatical alternative. He held up his reports until the last moment. This was accompanied by a variety of gastrointestinal symptoms. After some therapy he was able to hand in his reports after only one review. This greatly reduced the time involved, as well as his GI complaints. However, he became preoccupied with the errors he might have overlooked. Even when his supervisor complimented him on the task, he felt that it was not so outstanding as usual. In addition, he felt that while the work was accompanied by somewhat less anxiety, it was not much of an improvement. With repeated attempts at this report-writing pattern, the preoccupations lessened and the procedure became so much more acceptable that he soon began to act as if he had thought it all out and achieved the change all by himself.

The position the therapist must take in these early efforts is to convey the notion that there are no guarantees in living and that every new experience contains some risks—and may even turn out badly. While the therapist is trying to focus on the possible rewards and positive results of new adventures, he must avoid minimizing the risks or giving false guarantees of success. At times the therapist must make it clear that some risks must be taken and new behavior patterns must be tested for therapy to proceed. Obsessional ruminations and speculations produce no changes in outlook or in living; thus a patient must be actively encouraged and assisted in new ventures.

One patient with a severe obsessional pattern and a phobia of public speaking managed to benefit from therapy by making considerable changes in his life. However, he could not risk speaking in public places, particularly when he would be scheduled in advance. On one occasion, after having managed to evade several speaking engagements, he called to tell me of his concern about the continuation of this symptom, which was interfering with his professional life. We agreed that he would accept the next engagement and make every effort to keep it. This time he took neither tranquilizers nor alcohol to help him through the anxiety, but with encouragement and support, he endured the considerable anxiety and gave his talk—which was not so successful as he had hoped it would be. However, he felt enormously relieved, and was quite pleased with his accomplishment. He felt that he had finally licked his incapacitating phobic symptom. The willingness to endure some anxiety, which he had finally achieved, created the atmosphere for overcoming the demand for a perfect performance without anxiety or concern. While he will undoubtedly continue to have minor bouts with this difficulty for some time to come, the symptom should not greatly incapacitate him any longer.

MINIMIZING RISKS

Verbal speculation, a style of the obsessional, is an attempt to minimize the risks of failure; it often leads to more complications and greater insecurity. It can rarely overcome inaction. Real living in the face of real risks must be attempted through cautious encouragement by the therapist. The patient must not feel that failures will be viewed as disappointments by the therapist; therefore the therapist must avoid becoming too identified with the success or failure of a project even while he warmly supports the project itself. This is often very difficult, as the patient tries to prove his worthwhileness by demonstrating his skill to the therapist; a failure, he feels, will be interpreted by the therapist as a disappointment. Therefore, while indicating interest in the outcome of an activity, the therapist should avoid conveying any notion that rejection or criticism would follow a failure. There must be nothing more at stake for the patient than the task at hand; he should not have a feeling of ultimate judgment or disappointment should it not turn out well.

While such attempts at action are crucial to the successful outcome of therapy, they should not be made prematurely.

There should be sufficient possibility of a successful outcome in an activity that has been heretofore avoided before the patient is encouraged to engage in it. This can be determined either through some decrease in anxiety or in a patient's willingness to abandon his perfectionistic goal. There must also be a sufficient background of experience to make the project a feasible one. A patient who has never attempted to date a person of the opposite sex should be cautioned about premature attempts to date and his expectation of having an easy and successful time. Premature attempts may result in disastrous failures which then jeopardize the possibility of ultimately resolving the neurosis. Sometimes the patient will press for such activities and the resultant failure will be used as proof of the need to maintain his neurotic structure. The therapist must be alert to this maneuver and should forestall such adventures when they seem doomed to failure.

This was demonstrated by a severe obsessional who recognized that by not telling his business partner about some of his concerns he was jeopardizing their business; this was evident from examination of a number of occasions when he withheld his judgment on significant matters. However, he felt that I would be disappointed in him if he had another talk with his partner without telling him just how he felt. Therefore he pressed to do so. I informed him that I had no such expectation of him at this time and would feel no disappointment about it. However, I said that I was interested in his concerns about my reactions. (He was pushing prematurely for a full revelation of all his difficulties, which would have doomed the partnership and endangered his own existence. It was quite feasible to wait until he was better prepared to deal with the difficulties that might ensue from such a revelation.)

Many compulsive confessions which are often rationalized as the need to tell the whole truth in some abstract conception of honesty result in tragic consequences. An adolescent girl who was engaged to be married felt compelled to tell her fiance that she had kissed another boy and then went into a deep depression when the engagement was terminated.

Such premature or compulsive admissions or confessions in therapy are often called "acting out" and must be controlled by therapeutic intervention. This does not change the notion that the obsessional should be encouraged to action when he is ready for it and is not restrained by his obsessional need for guarantees.

Unless a patient is ready to attempt new ventures, it is unwise and unfruitful for the therapist to press the patient to make a decision; this would only produce further rationalizations and justifications for avoidance. Instead, the therapist must explore the question of the patient's caution and his demand for absolutes in his living. When the patient does make a decision, it should be an outgrowth of the consideration of these factors rather than his need to comfort or please the therapist or to prove that he is capable of taking some action.

When an obsessional patient finally manages a new piece of behavior, he often sets it up in such a way as to minimize his responsibilities for a failure. Any failure is blamed on the therapist who, the patient insists, forced him to do something he was clearly not ready to do. On the other hand, if such behavior is successful, the patient will assume full credit and ignore the role which the therapist played in the matter. It is not particularly useful to clarify this situation too early or to emphasize the role of the therapy as it may introduce too many extraneous factors —such as the need to take credit for the success. When the patient has experienced some real success in his new ventures and has a degree of self-assurance, then the collaborative aspect of the work needs to be emphasized in order to put the patient's grandiose tendencies in some perspective. The tendency to pass the responsibility for failure on to the therapist can lead to endless squabbles and unwarranted attacks on him. The need of the patient to "pass the buck" should be noted, and full responsibility for any proposed action must be placed squarely on the patient's shoulders. While this will not remove the possibility of the therapist's being blamed, it does leave him free and able to state his position simply—without getting involved in a fruitless exchange of whose fault the failure is. The point in therapy is to encourage action and involvement; at the same time, it is important for the therapist to reduce the neurotic elements in his own involvement even when he must get involved in order to clarify the "transfer of blame" distortions of the obsessional patient—particularly as they blend into paranoid ideas. Such involvements are invaluable sources of illumination of the obsessional defense and the tendency to transfer blame onto others.

PROBLEMS OF DOUBTING

The obsessional's pervasive tendency to doubt and hence to procrastinate activity manifests itself throughout the therapeutic process, and at times may defeat it. The patient may question each observation or interpretation and cast an aura of uncertainty over any exchange—especially if it is enlightening or disturbing to him. In short, the presence of doubt must be noted and dealt with throughout the entire therapeutic work.

Doubting also interferes with any effective action in the patient's current living. It prevents firm commitments; hence the patient may put off an action, attempting to get the therapist to overcome such doubts and make the decesion for him. If he succeeds in doing this, he still retains his doubts about the decision, secretly opposing it because he did not make the choice himself. He will covertly sabotage it; thereby the effort will fail, proving that the choice was an error. Therefore the therapist must be especially careful not to be drawn into this trap. Any attempt to eliminate the patient's doubts by a rational examination of the alternatives is clearly doomed to failure; the doubts do not arise as a result of some dilemma in which the alternatives are intellectual choices. It is not the rational or objective appraisal of the pros and cons of an issue which stimulates valid doubts about a choice. Therefore, the doubts cannot be resolved by a careful consideration of the situation. A cataloging or bookkeeping of all the issues would be endless and would increase the doubting instead of overcoming it. Every advantage on one side can be countered by an advantage on the other, as can the disadvantages. Such intellectual exploration of alternatives is a very successful device for avoiding a decision.

To deal with this obstacle in therapy it would be reasonable to assume that some insight into the origins and genetic history of the doubting might decrease its effect on the person's living. However, the attempt to explore the origins of the patient's doubting is generally fruitless; it does not arise as a result of a single or multiple event in the past. Nor does it have any origins in a once-meaningful context which, if discovered, would clarify its origins. Such a search, if undertaken, would be obstructed by the very doubting itself—which would minimize any conviction about the discoveries that might be made.

Doubting is a baffling and overwhelming complication in the therapy of obsessionals. It makes every investigation uncertain and every statement or interpretation open to question. The doubts are often secretly maintained and brought out into the open only when necessary. Covertly they may be used to minimize the therapist's insights and to help the patient remain aloof and uninvolved with the therapist and the therapeutic process. The doubts create an atmosphere of tentativeness toward the whole process; therefore they must be exposed early if therapy is to progress. However, as a device, doubting cannot be investigated as a fact in itself. This will result in getting the process bogged down in unproductive preoccupations and further doubting. It must be studied as a part of the patient's living, not as a separate item, and must be brought to his attention as it manifests itself in all his activities and relationships.

As the doubting is a device to guarantee certainty and to avoid a decision when certainty is impossible, it will remain in the picture until the security needs of the patient are sufficiently enhanced so that he can take some risks and accept some uncertainty.

The therapist must encourage the patient to arrive at decisions based on an *emotional* appeal of the alternatives as well as on an intellectual appraisal. Such a step follows from awareness that all choices have emotional as well as intellectual sources and that choice cannot be solely an intellectual process. As decision making is already a burdensome problem for the obsessional, any encouragement to admit emotional factors into his living can be a most constructive prospect.

The therapist should encourage the patient to make any decision—even a poor decision is better than none at all. Moreover, he must help the patient to recognize that dreadful consequences need not follow an imperfect decision.

The question, "Which alternative do you like?" has greater validity than, "Which alternative is the better choice?" The obsessional has difficulty in raising this question because his decisions must be correct rather than pleasing or satisfying. However, the consideration of which alternative would be least pleasureable or satisfying must enter the decision-making process, in addition to which is the correct alternative. This is clearly a most difficult problem for the obsessional, who feels that only intellectual considerations can guarantee the correctness of a choice. Emotions, he contends, are too easily pushed about by forces that cannot be controlled. Nevertheless, the patient must be encouraged to realize that emotional considerations must enter the decision-making process and that they are often major ingredients. Many choices are matters of taste or preference rather than economy or wisdom. There needs also to be a lightness and casualness in the patient's decision-making process—especially when such decisions do not touch on core issues or can be altered without major damage to the individual.

It is also evident that one can never assemble all the relevant factors in any situation in order to make a perfect choice. Alternatives can be so evenly matched that only the emotional factors of preference, prejudice, or pure *feeling* will be the final factor. On such occasions, the therapist, in encouraging the patient to make a choice, must be clear about his own predilections, prejudices, and inclinations in order to avoid covertly influencing the patient's decision.

Ultimately, doubting will come to play a less significant role in the therapeutic process as the patient's security and esteem are enhanced. The doubts are an adaptive technique and not elements of integrity in the obsessional's personality structure, and should be distinguished from the real uncertainties that prevail in human existence. Not every uncertainty is a morbid doubt. In the therapy of the obsessional this distinction becomes quite important because we wish to encourage valid uncertainties in contrast to the kind of insistence on certainty which requires morbid doubting.

The therapist must try to encourage real questioning while trying to eliminate the neurotic doubting. He must, however, avoid dealing with the doubts as if they represented valid and rational uncertainties. Therefore, a detailed examination of alternatives in every situation, which the obsessional will always insist upon, and the attempts to explore all the issues exhaustively to arrive at perfect decisions is an utter waste of time. It is not a matter of exposing the issues so that the patient can then see the facts which will allow him to decide and forego his doubts; rather there is a need to show him that the doubts are attempts to make infallible decisions regardless of the issues.

A Note of Caution

However, the fact must not be overlooked that many decisions and choices have realistic factors which need to be taken into account and that not all considerations of alternatives are instances of obsessional doubting. There are valid uncertainties owing to lack of information, which must be acknowledged and recognized. Unless this is done we cannot communicate to the patient about his excesses which go beyond the legitimate task of exploring all the realistic alternatives. In addition, some uncertainties of the patient, such as whether he is really liked, or what he truly wants, must be viewed in a different light from doubts that arise in a situation in which the expectation of certainty and exemption from natural law is expected. Before one can convince the obsessional that this indecision is based on neurotic grounds and not on actual alternatives, and that his pre-occupations and concerns are excessive and not in response to real issues, one must hear enough of the patient's account to consider all these possibilities. In this way the patient will be convinced that the realistic issues have been taken into account. This is especially important because while the therapist can quickly identify the concern as obsessional, the patient still believes it is based on fact and justified by circumstances. One must hear the story out even when it is quickly understood that the concerns are excessive and not responsive to the actual circumstances. After a while one can use a short-cut, saying, "Now isn't that just like so and so, which was really your neurotic indecision, rather than a serious consideration of the alternatives?" The patient may agree, or is likely to say: "No, this is different." But we need to hear enough to show him that it is not different. One must have the patience to recognize that the obsessional learns slowly, if at all, and must hear repeated instances of a particular interpretation before he can really accept it.

PROBLEMS OF INDECISION

The indecision of the obsessional is closely related to his morbid doubts. As he requires certainty in every choice he must make and is unwilling to take any risks, it is understandable that he puts off making a decision until he can feel absolutely sure.

He must be very careful, since he presumes that every decision will tie him down permanently, with no way out. This accounts for his tentative acceptance of the exchanges in the therapeutic process; nothing is seen or experienced with any degree of closure, but remains open to alteration or reversal. Therefore interpretations are rarely accepted with conviction or full agreement, but with a qualifying, uncertain uneasiness. It is indecision which keeps the obsessive from coming into therapy early. Once in, however, he may remain endlessly and be unable to leave unless an adequate handling of the therapeutic situation forces a change. The usual instructions to forego any decision during therapy and to postpone living until more valid decisions can be made play directly into his neurotic pattern. Many obsessionals who should benefit greatly from the psychotherapeutic process—it is the treatment of choice for this neurosis—find a haven for their neurosis and a reinforcement of their defenses because of inadequate or inept therapeutic handling in this regard. The obsessional prefers to take no action. Thus, psychotherapy, under certain conditions, can become an ideal culture for the enhancement of obsessional doubts and indecisions. It is only in recent years that psychoanalysts have begun to recognize that the routine therapeutic techniques are not suitable for all types of character structures and sometimes need to be adjusted to the particular characteristics of the personality involved. The obsessional should be encouraged to arrive at conclusions and to make decisions which are the product of a reasonable and adequate exploration of the relevant factors. The technique for dealing with the patient's indecisiveness involves the need to clarify his quest for absolutes and certainties.

It must be recognized that the postponement of living in order to guarantee the best and wisest decision often takes a higher toll than making some decision, even if it is not the most perfect one. Imperfect decisions may be the best that one can reach at a particular time. The obsessional dresses up his indecision in intellectual rationalizations that imply strength rather than weakness, and the virtues of honesty and integrity rather than fear and uncertainty. A helpful therapeutic atmosphere, therefore, would encourage movement and activity—both in and out of the therapeutic situation—and would cautiously advocate decisions in the patient's living. While therapy should always restrain premature or impulsive behavior, it should not encourage postponing activities on purely theoretical grounds.

A patient who got caught in an indecisive conflict over a professional choice is illustrative. She needed to decide between two geographical areas for her next assignment and had a reasonable amount of time in which to make the decision. After considering all the realistic differences which could be determined, she arrived at a tentative decision which was inconsistent with the emotional ties she had to these areas. She then reversed her decision. Having done this, she began to feel uneasy and more confident about her first choice. She was concerned about the frivolous way in which she had changed her mind. At this time her obsessional indecisiveness was in full swing, with her anxiety increasing as the final day arrived. She tried to explore every phase of the choice, taking into account which would be the better opportunity, which would offer the better climate, and which would have the larger number of museums, swimming facilities, travel opportunities, available boyfriends, etc. Every consideration was explored, both relevant and irrelevant. The harder she tried, the more impossible it was to make a decision. Yet her choice did not have permanent consequences—she could shift if her preference turned out badly. She exaggerated the significance of the factors involved in the choice as well as the consequences.

Everything involved in the choice was of the greatest seriousness; there was an absence of any lightness. She turned this moderately important decision into a laborious, life-or-death issue. As the final day approached, she began to get quite panicky. The emphasis which she placed on making the "right" decision helped her to see how this factor affected all the decisions in her life and why she had always been so indecisive. It finally dawned on her that success would come from work and achievement, and not from the magic of the right choice.

Now a flood of new factors entered into her calculations, and she wished she could withdraw her decision. Her reaction was similar to the "undoing" of a ritual once it has been performed, which is associated with the uncertainty about the act once it has been performed. Therefore, there is the necessity to neutralize it for fear it may be the wrong act. In this case the patient could not rest with either choice as she could not accept the possible disadvantages of either one.

I encouraged this patient to make some decision after we had fully explored the realistic differences in each alternative.

I stressed the need for some choice, as it was not possible to foresee all the future advantages of either. I implied that there was no ideal decision, no matter how detailed or complete her consideration could be. She accused me of trying to force her to make premature decisions and of not being really interested in her career and her success. At the same time she acknowledged that if I pushed a particular choice, she would hold me responsible for any dissatisfactions she might find with it. I was most careful to indicate no preference, either covertly or overtly.

In such instances, the therapist, after an initial survey of the alternatives, must restrict his observations to the question of the patient's need to make the perfect decision and not get involved in what that might be. The patient must recognize that all the pros and cons which he introduces as intelligent and rational steps in the decision process are actually attempts to avoid making a decision. They are measures designed to produce a perfect decision in order to prevent unfavorable consequences. As a perfect decision is impossible, the patient must acknowledge that any choice involves risks.

Too much of the obsessional's time is spent in preparation and in laying the groundwork for the expected success in some career. This patient's success was delayed for many years because her preparations and academic work would shift from year to year so that she could cover al the possibilities. She developed a smattering of knowledge in many areas and an expertness in none. To specialize in one area she would have to eliminate another, and this she could not do. It took her a long time to realize that any decision would be to her advantage in the long run and would be better than spending her time trying to find the perfect one. Fortunately, time and circumstances often push these people into decisions which, once they are made, can be fruitfully exploited.

Because it is humiliating to face the weakness and ineffectiveness involved in procrastination, obsessionals easily transfer the blame for their indecisiveness onto wives, family, parents, community, etc. They rationalize their indecision by claiming that they cannot decide because they are either concerned with the best interest of others, or they have been so thwarted in early years that making decisions is too difficult. It becomes part of the therapist's task to illuminate all these distracting techniques and to focus on the real issue—the patient's demand for omniscient, superhuman performance.

With regard to the patient's tendency to "use" the therapist for his decision-making processes and as his whipping boy when the decisions turn out badly, the therapist must make it clear time and again that he has no stake other than a professional concern and interest in the welfare of the patient, and that he has no purpose or design directed at reducing the patient's goals or aspirations.

While it is possible for some useful therapeutic work to take place when there is only a minimal amount of warmth between patient and therapist, progress is undoubtedly enhanced if there is more rather than less. The positive attitudes of patient for therapist must be routinely utilized in the thera- is particularly relevant because premature or clumsy disclosures peutic process. In the treatment of the obsessive patient, this of the therapist's feelings might impress the patient as a weakness of the therapist and an expression of his need to seduce the patient or take advantage of him. It could be viewed as an expression of the therapist's anxiety—for which the patient might feel contempt. Timing and an appropriate mode of expression are crucial elements in communicating such feelings to the patient. This is particularly necessary when the patient tries out new patterns of behavior. The therapist's interest can be a source of encouragement. As much of the therapeutic work deals with efforts to get the patient to reveal his true feelings and not only his intellectualized verbalizations, the therapist must set the tone and show the way by being frank and open about his feelings toward the patient. While for some therapists the obsessive patient may be hard to like, one can generally find many likeable qualities. Some of the therapist's interest in changing his patient's way of life is not only the result of professional pride or status, but also of warm and affectionate feelings for the patient. Whenever change is attempted, it must come from the patient's interest in his own development and not because of gratitude toward the therapist or as a way of impressing him. It must emerge from a real desire to alter one's living, and not just to please someone or to prove something. Change is encouraged and often promoted by an affectionate interest of one person toward another. This is one of the ingredients of a therapeutic relationship. The therapist's attitudes should reinforce the real aspirations of the patient by highlighting those neurotic elements which interfere with the attainment of achievable goals.

As he improves, the patient must be able—through his growing confidence in the therapist and an expanding trust in his own capabilities—to accept the risks and consequences of his new behavioral patterns. He must be able to face the possibility of his worst fears being realized—that he might feel humiliated or look weak and impotent in his new ways of functioning. He must be wiling to abandon complete control of a project and allow a situation to develop on its own, often with no certainty of the outcome. Giving up control does not mean becoming apathetic or withdrawing. It means a more realistic acceptance of the world as it is, as a place where one must accept uncertainties in living. The resolution of an obsessional disorder should produce a more mature, more decisive and accepting, and less driven human being—not an emotionless, placid philosopher. The process can be assisted most dramatically by a warm and interested therapist who can inspire in his patient an intellectual grasp of the neurotic issues as well as the real issues and encourage acknowledgement of feelings in a direct and open way.

RITUALS

The ritualistic behavior of the patient, whether it is in the form of a compulsive action or an obsessional rumination, must be dealt with in the same way as the doubting tendencies. The rituals represent attempts at achieving certainty or preventing the person from losing control in some significant area of his living. They involve not only aggressive or sexual impulses but tender impulses as well.

The attempts at understanding the precise meaning of the ritual may be an interesting intellectual exercise, but in general it will not advance the therapeutic process to any appreciable extent. The same problems which stem from investigating the origin of the doubting also apply in the instance of rituals.

While the symbolic meaning of this ritual can often be inferred from the various elements in it, an intellectual elucidation of the symbolic acts seldom, if ever, alters the ritual. The classical hand-washing ritual, for example, can be correctly interpreted as an attempt to be rid of dangerous germs or sexual contamination. It could represent attempts to wash away the guilt or the symbolic blood of a fantasized victim. On the other hand, it could be a device for keeping the person preoccupied and thereby prevent him from getting on with his living. The particular ritual employed may be entirely accidental or coincidental and may have significance only in terms of the setting in which a severe anxiety attack may have occurred. The hand-washing ritual may be a device to avoid the recognition of the possibility of death and may have begun when the person was forced to face the early death of a friend because of some infectious disease. The proper interpretation of the ritual, however, does not influence its continuation; its real roots lie in deep-seated feelings of uncertainty about one's safety and security. The understanding of the purpose of the ritual may be easy and readily accepted by the patient. He may often offer the correct explanation himself. However, this rarely influences the course of the neurosis or the continuation of the ritual. At other times the ritual may be so autistic and complicated that its elucidation is impossible.

Generally, the search for the origin of the ritual is not worth the time spent; it can be better explored in other contexts.

The existence of the ritual depends entirely on the individual's capacity to abandon his absolute needs in order to control his own feelings through magical performances. Intellectual clarifications and statements about the patient's wasting his time, energy, and skill in these rituals are to no avail. The patient is generally fully aware of all these facts. However, the serious complications resulting from the rituals may pressure the patient to end them, and he may press the therapist to exorcise them by direct intervention. Such demands often push the therapist to become preoccupied with the rituals themselves, which may impede the ultimate and more significant therapeutic goal.

One way of evading the therapeutic relationship is for the patient to become preoccupied with descriptions and detailed explanations of the ritual. Unless the therapist can recognize the purpose and terminate these recitals, they may occupy the bulk of the therapeutic work. The presence of many rituals in a patient is some indication of the severity of the obsessional illness and generally implies a poor prognosis, while a paucity of rituals suggest a less severe personality disorder. In either case, the fate of the ritual is tied to the over-all treatment progress, and the patient must be so informed right from the beginning.

The ritual will be abandoned when the patient's need for magic and ultimate control of himself and the universe is lessened. The therapist's handling of the ritual involves his ability to understand the role that it plays in the patient's life. When the patient persists in projecting it into the therapeutic process, it becomes the responsibility of the therapist to discourage repeition with the explanation that it is more of a distraction than an aid to resolution of the illness. If the ritual is particularly incapacitating, one might try to attack it directly and attempt either to eliminate it or alter it. In doing this, however, one must be clear that the basis for the development of the ritual has been unchanged even though its presence may have been eliminated.

RESOLUTIONS

For a long time the obsessional deals with therapy as if it were designed to improve his neurosis rather than to alter it.

Even though the initial goal of becoming perfect through the therapeutic process may be abandoned, the patient will try for some time to overcome his compulsions, which are now viewed as "bad," or destructive, by replacing them with "good" or constructive ones. When he discovers that the trouble is that he is compelled to be perfect, he will henceforth *resolve* never to be perfect. He simply alters all his previous extreme demands by resolving not to make any demands at all. As he functions by commands and great resolves, he simply shifts emphasis from a "bad" resolve to a "good" one. Because so much of obsessional behavior is the result of compulsion over which the obsessional has no choice, he attempts to deal with the compulsion through a counter-compulsion. He now resolves to do the right thing. It is clear that this shift represents no essential change in the patient's personality or behavior, and this fact must be brought to his attention. The patient justifiably insists that he can only overcome the power of his compulsions through resolve and action. The clue to this psychological bind lies in the patient's recognition that not all behavior is the result of conscious and deliberate decision and that the obsessional illness is itself proof of this. Therefore, he cannot overcome behavior that arises from unconscious sources by conscious intent. Instead of making new resolutions to overcome the compulsions, he should abandon all resolutions—conscious and otherwise. He must simply do the best he can instead of insisting on perfection. This is experienced by the patient as the advocacy of inaction and weakness. Instead, it is encouraging the patient (as in Zen) to "let go" and just allow an experience to happen rather than trying to make it happen. While the patient does not take to this program readily, he must learn to do so as it is essential for the clarification of his disorder.

The patient insists that to forego the highest standards means that he will have to accept the lowest. It is the fear of nothingness, mediocrity, and total unconcern which forces him to cling to his rigid, extreme demands. Therefore, when it becomes clear to the patient that he should not feel he needs to do every job perfectly, he may resolve not to insist on perfection but to accept imperfection. With perfect control, and using new rituals and variations of his obsessional technique, he will insist on imperfections.

It is essential to point out to the patient at this juncture that he is substituting one compulsion for another. He must recognize and feel that what is needed is to see that one does not have to be perfect or to have compulsions about imperfections, but to be able to accept human limitations and to realize that one can only do the best one can. The obsessional patient will undoubtedly say, "What do you want me to do, settle for nothing and do a sloppy job?" He might also say that he cannot accept ordinary standards of mediocrity and accuse the therapist of trying to deflate and derogate him. After considerable discussion, the patient may finally acknowledge his deep concern about abandoning any of his extreme needs—even though he recognizes the impossibility of attaining them. The therapeutic impasse at this point can be resolved only by indicating that it is not "all or none" and that there are other alternatives aside from the extreme ones which he posits. The therapist must convince the patient that he has no demands to make on him other than to assist him in fulfilling his own realistic goals. The patient must be convinced that if he abandons his extremes, he would not be disappointed but rather would be pleased at the favorable development. Indeed, it must be dramatically seen that as the result of the patient's greater esteem and security, which allow him to give up unrealistic goals for realizable projects, he can experience greater satisfaction.

DREAMS

The analysis of dreams in the therapy of the obsessional must take into account the above-discussed tendencies to evade and obfuscate the therapeutic process. It must also take into account the readiness of the patient to comply and win favor with the therapist by supplying dreams. Therefore, if the therapist puts undue stress on dreams or displays any special interest in them he may be flooded with dream material which could, if one wished, take up all the time in therapy. There are no particular characteristics of the obsessional's dreams. They reflect the life problems and the emotional relationships of the patient with the therapist, friends, etc., as all dreams do. They also utilize the particular techniques of defense in the dreams which are characteristic of the patient's waking life. As so much of the obsessional's life is preoccupied with problems of control, it will not be surprising to find that much of the dream material concerns itself with control.

The dreams need to be handled in the same way as are the dreams of other patients. The dream content should be examined in terms of the "here and now" and as it sheds light on the current living of the patient. The tendency to get deeply involved in understanding all the associations and every bit of detail can become a trap for the therapist. It can turn into an obsessional investigation in which the ultimate effect is to become distracted from the main pursuit.

Because dreams can be very illuminating with regard to sources and unacknowledged feelings and attitudes, their use in the therapeutic process should not be discouraged. At the same time, they must be treated as simple data and dealt with in the same way as other productions of the patient. (The handling of dream material in general, and obsessional dream material in particular, is discussed in detail by Bonime in his book *The Clinical Use of Dreams*, which is highly recommended to the reader.)

The dream of a 42-year-old obsessional patient illustrates the points mentioned above. She came into therapy because she felt that she was too controlling in her relationship with her daughter. She spent a considerable amount of therapeutic time complaining about her resentments and hostilities toward her own mother. At about her seventh hour she reported a dream which occurred on the previous evening after she had attended a movie with her husband and daughter. Only front row seats were available in the theatre, and she had indicated to her husband that she would prefer to return another time. Her daughter, however, preferred to stay. Without making any comment to his wife, the husband purchased the tickets and proceeded to enter the theatre. Although angry and resentful toward her daughter, the patient made no comment either to her daughter or to her husband. In therapy on the following day she reported that she felt that she had over-reacted to her daughter, and reported having had the following dream:

"I was in our house at Cape Cod with my family. Mother was there. Two uninvited guests arrived and I asked mother to fix the steaks. While I was bawling her out for not doing the steaks properly, I completely ruined the casserole dish I was making." While it is clear from her report about the movie and the dream that she has many problems in her relationship with her husband, mother, and daughter, the therapist's emphasis in the interpretation at that time was limited to her tendency to displace her anger at both her daughter and her mother and to avoid recognizing that in doing this she was damaging herself. This was the focus of most of the reports during the first six sessions.

Her need to control her anger in the movie incident prevented any clarification of the relevant issues. At that time her anger was not an over-reaction to her daughter. She was quite justified in being angry at her husband, who had paid no attention to her request and had disregarded her wishes completely. (This, incidentally, was her complaint about all the men in her life.) In the dream, too, she displaced her anger from the uninvited guests (whose identity could not be established) to her mother. She got angry at her mother for spoiling the steaks rather than being angry at herself for ruining the family dinner (the casserole). Her tendency to displace her anger was the cause of the disaster; the casserole burned because she was preoccupied with the anger toward her mother.

Both the movie incident and the dream were rich sources

of data in exploring many of this patient's problems of control and displacement of anger. In limiting the scope of the interpretations at that time, the patient could grasp the essence of her behavior and have a solid piece of insight with convincing affectual response.

Another example was that of a 35-year-old man who felt that he was overly competitive. This was how he accounted for his hostile and alienated relationships with both men and women. It was a formula and rationale for his socializing failures, but it did not influence his living in any respect.

He reported a dream in which he found himself somewhat isolated at a party. He felt quite sorry for himself. But soon everyone left and he was alone with three attractive young ladies. He now became quite aggressive when the most attractive girl made overt sexual gestures toward him, to which he responded. He reported that it was a pleasant dream even though he felt uneasy about his behavior. The dream and the patient's association to it were explored from the point of view of current material which was being dealt with during previous therapy hours. The dream was seen as an instance of his tendency to avoid competition instead of seeking it out. When he was with the larger group, he isolated himself; when he was alone with the girls he became aggressive and energetic. This interpretation opened up a new view of himself as a rather arrogant and egocentric person who avoids competition and feels entitled to get what he wants. Instead of being competitive, he feels that he should automatically have exclusive possession of whatever he needs or wishes. This grandiose view of himself, which he secretly held, was brought out into the open. It had been covered up by his picture of himself as a man with a great deal of humility and a tendency to be uneasy in his relationships. Actually, he felt resentful because his needs were not automatically filled and because he needed to exert some effort to get what he wanted. Some relevant factors revealed in the dream —such as the doubts about his masculinity, his notions of his desirability, and his anxieties about being rejected and humiliated—were bypassed for the moment. To make the maximum use of a dream, its interpretation should be related to the material current in the therapy hours and restricted to a few major issues which can be explored sufficiently to provide some conviction about the validity of the interpretation.

PHOBIAS

The treatment of the phobias is closely related to the therapy of the obsessional state, as the two disorders are dynamically similar. However, the phobia may be either a minor element in the patient's problems or in the disability imposed by the phobia, which may be so overwhelming as to demand the focus of the therapeutic process. In the usual course of events, the phobias accompanying the obsessional processes may either become less troublesome or disappear in the course of treatment, requiring no special handling. As the need to exert control over all of one's living diminishes and there is a growing capacity to accept the limitations in one's existence without having guarantees and certainties, the phobic symptoms also diminish.

When this does not occur, we must then take some direct action and deal directly with the phobia. It has been known for some time that understanding alone has been ineffectual in resolving phobias. It is commonplace that while the patient may have adequate insight into the origin, symbolism, and function of his phobia, he is still unable to risk the initial venture into this heretofore out-of-bounds area of living. This fact has stimulated much discussion about the issue of intellectual versus emotional insight, and particularly about the need for some "corrective emotional experience" (as Franz Alexander called it) to accompany the therapeutic process.

After some intellectual and emotional clarity about the phobic problem has been achieved, the major task is to encourage and assist the patient into entering and reexperiencing those areas of living which he has avoided. As the problem goes beyond mere fear, intellectual persuasion or sympathetic assurances will not suffice. As the phobia is more than a conditioned response to fear, "deconditioning" through the reciprocal inhibition techniques only serves to remove specific fears; it does not alter the phobic state. While great claims are made for this treatment technique, it is my belief that it influences "bad habits" rather than true phobias. As explained in an earlier chapter, the phobia is different from the simple avoidance reaction that results from a severe traumatic situation and has overriding physiological concomitants; thus the elucidation of the trauma, by hypnosis, will not alter its manifestations as it so dramatically does in avoidance reactions.

A combination of persuasive and encouraging techniques can be very fruitful. Once he has achieved sufficient insight, the patient must be directly encouraged and at times actively assisted to attempt to invade the phobic areas. However, if such pressure for activity is not accompanied by sufficient understanding or support, the phobic problem may be exaggerated by the development of severe anxiety, which will reinforce the determination to resist change.

There are many possible ways of actively encouraging a patient to move into previously avoided areas. First, the therapist can use the potential in the positive transference which has developed in the course of treatment. Provided the patient has achieved some benefit from the therapeutic work in alleviating some of his obsessional difficulties, he may have some confidence in the possibility of change. At such times, he may be willing to risk anxiety in order to discover that the rewards for undoing the phobia may be greater than the anticipated anxiety. This is not an easy matter, and it may be necessary to call on the good will, trust, and confidence that the patient has developed in his therapist. Admittedly, this is a risky procedure for the therapist as well; if the maneuver fails, much work will need to be done to reverse the damage. Yet the therapist, as well as the patient, must take risks and must not expect guarantees or certainties.

On such occasions, the encouragement must be direct and energetic. While one should not minimize the risks, the positive possibilities must be highlighted. The support may, at times, involve accompanying the patient into the phobic area. On one occasion, I accompanied a patient with a phobia of open spaces into the street, walked with her awhile, and then left her to return to the office alone. In some instances, tranquillizing drugs or even alcohol may be used to encourage the initial attempts. With some success, the way is opened for further attempts, and finally for the abandonment of the phobia.

Posthypnotic suggestions can be used to induce a phobic person to explore a phobic area. However, in such an instance the relationship develops specifically around the treatment of the phobia and does not sufficiently recognize the obsessional elements in the symptom.

Some therapists utilize the phobic's need to control all his living by entering into the phobic way of life—taking over the running of the show and putting the patient in the background. This stimulates the patient's rebelliousness as well as his competitive needs, and he may abandon the phobia just to demonstrate his control. This is simply a manipulative device. While it may work, it only strengthens the obsessional patterns and may provide a greater source of difficulty at a later date.

In recent years, phenomenological analysts such as Viktor Frankl and H. O. Gerz have used a technique called *paradoxical intention* most successfully in the resolution of phobic states. This method takes into account the compulsive, unfree nature of the phobic avoidance. Against his will and free choice, the patient avoids a situation, place, or person, even while knowing it is absurd and irrational to do so. However, he must pursue the phobic demands because the threat of anxiety is so great. The paradoxical intention technique forces the patient to accept the phobia willingly and deliberately and put it under voluntary control. This focuses on the absurdity of the symptom and also gives the person the possibility of controlling its manifestations by putting it squarely under his responsibility. While the paradoxical nature of a therapist's encouraging his patient to continue his symptom is most evident, the real issue is in terms of putting the action under the patient's choice and under his control. Because many of the phobic symptoms are expressed through the autonomic nervous system, such feelings and functions are not under voluntary control. Therefore, when the patient tries to produce his symptom, as he is instructed to do, he usually fails. When he finds that he is unable to produce his symptom, it frequently disappears. This technique does not remove the symptom at once; it must be repeated over a long period of time because reconditioning is also involved in the permanent eradication of the phobia. By encouraging the patient to get worse instead of better, he is freed from his symptom. This treatment draws on the element of control and the issue of free will and choice. The technique has also been applied to the treatment of the obsessive states, but with less success. It is intended to supplement psychotherapy, not to replace it.

In summary, the treatment of phobias—in addition to providing insight and enlightenment—requires some direct encouragement through sympathy or persuasion to reexperience the phobic fear. The encouragement may be in terms of the personal and professional relationship of patient and therapist, or through some device such as conditioning, posthypnotic suggestion, or stimulation of paradoxical intention. In all instances success lies in the recognition that once a phobia develops, there must be some incentive to face anxiety, uncertainty, and discomfort through the helping presence of an interested, sympathetic helper.

TERMINATION

When the patient comes to therapy his goal is to achieve a state of anxiety-free living while retaining the same collection of personality traits that he had originally. During the course of therapy, the patients must recognize the extreme nature of his demands and accept some limitations of his expectations. It is hoped that he will be able to achieve some balance and compromise; instead of having to be a superman, he will be able to function as a fallible human being. This simplified picture of the therapeutic goal of treatment of the obsessional provides some clues as to guidelines in determining a termination date.

At the outset, the therapist must not have a set of ideal standards for his patient to meet. He should be able to express flexible and limited goals, to avoid getting involved in the same problems of perfection which are the patient's to begin with. While there is some pressure on the part of the patient to leave therapy and to function on his own, there is also great reluctance to give up the comfortable world of talk and move into the real world of action until he is absolutely certain that no insurmountable problems will occur. The patient will often insist on remaining in therapy, and the therapist will need to prod and push him into the world. In the obsessional neuroses we find the long, interminable analyses which have often become symbiotic relationships instead of doctor-patient ones. Termination plans cannot be left to the patient, as is often the case with other kinds of patients. Obsessional patients cannot be relied upon to raise the question or to press for termination on their own.

What are the criteria for assessing termination? First, there must be a recognition that termination must be done gradually and experimentally, and rarely in an absolute way. To begin with, the number of interview hours can be cut down, or the frequency reduced over a reasonable period of time. This will help the therapist to determine whether a date can be set for ultimate termination. Experimental reductions in therapy hours can begin when the patient becomes comfortable enough to accept some reverses in his living which heretofore stimulated panic or severe anxiety. There should also be a reduction of tension in many areas of his living, coupled with a greater emotional involvement in all his relationships. There should also be evidence of reduction in ritualistic behavior, and many of the obsessions which plagued the patient when he came to treatment should have become less tenacious or no longer occur. There should be an increased capacity to enjoy life without having to fulfill certain demands all the time. But even these criteria should be flexible. The therapist must not get trapped into postponing or abandoning his plans to terminate because the patient gets a renewed anxiety attack when termination is under consideration. It must be clearly understood by both patient and therapist that anxiety attacks will occur throughout the life of the patient and that therapy is not a permanent guarantee against disturbed living.

When anxiety does occur, the therapist should not be stampeded into changing his arrangements, thus exposing his own demands for perfection—even though such a crisis may require some temporary acceleration of treatment. The decision to terminate cannot be decided by the fate of some particular symptom. This is especially true in the case of the psychosomatic symptoms which are so common in the obsessional disorders. Gastrointestinal disorders, cardiovascular problems, and symptoms of all sorts may clear up in the course of therapy without any particular emphasis being placed upon them. Some symptoms, however, may continue no matter how successful the therapy may be. Psychosomatic symptoms are usually the consequences of ever-present tension which characterizes the obsessional picture. Ordinarily, as the tension diminishes, the somatic symptoms improve. If, however, the somatic problems have continued for too long a time, they may be irreversible, and will continue after many other characterological problems are resolved. Therefore, their status should not, in general, determine the decision for termination.

After a formal termination, there should be ample opportunities for occasional visits and brief contacts at times of particular stress or crisis. It is hoped that in the process of therapy the patient will have developed sufficient skills in introspection (as opposed to preoccupation and rumination) so that new problems can be approached in an analytic fashion, enabling the person to proceed without resuming formal contacts.

Treatment of the obsessional patient is an extremely difficult task. Even minimal changes, however, are worth the investments of time and energy of both patient and therapist. Freedom from compulsions is often accompanied by a freeing of the individual's capacities so that he becomes a more effectively functioning person. In contrast to his initial fears, the abandonment of his unreal standards and expectations leads to more creative productions rather than a loose and unproductive existence. Freud's original conjecture was that obsessionalism was a neurotic problem which responded to psychoanalytic treatment; this belief has been amply documented in spite of the enormous difficulties and the extended time which is necessary. No other approach—including shock therapy, lobotomy, drugs, or the use of other devices—has detracted from the value of a psychotherapeutic approach to this disorder. Psychotherapy is the treatment modality which can and does effectively reduce the enormous anguish and waste that is inherent in obsessionalism.

The therapy of the obsessional state involves illuminating and exposing the patient's extreme feelings of insecurity and uncertainty—which he tries to handle through the complicated patterns of defense already described in detail. As he comes to understand his neurotic structure as a defense against recognizing these weaknesses, he can then begin to build a new security system. At therapy's inception, the obsessional defense cannot be abandoned because the individual is afraid of the consequences. As his esteem grows and the awareness of his strength increases, he can slowly risk abandoning such patterns and be freed to function on a more productive level. The goal is to move from superhuman expectations to human productiveness—which can reach whatever limits the individual is capable of. When he recovers, his ambitions will no longer be sparked by his neurosis; rather, his achievements will be limited only by his capacities. The impossible goals which left him disappointed will be abandoned. An awareness of his valid capacities to produce may actually stimulate greater activity. In essence, the obsessional must learn that in abandoning rigid, inflexible patterns of behavior designed to control and protect himself, he can actually feel more secure and more capable—and be more productive as well.

Such a change was demonstrated by a severely obsessional patient who was dangerously depressed when he entered therapy. His standards were extreme and his goals impossible, but his pride and his security system demanded that he hold to both. His original crisis arose when he was unable to communicate his feelings toward his partner; he felt crushed in his desire to liberate himself. After therapy had proceeded for some time, he began to feel sufficiently secure to attempt such a discussion. With great trepidation, but with a feeling of willingness to face the possible disastrous consequences, he undertook the discussion. To his surprise, the results were strikingly successful. There was great relief in the accomplishment; the successful outcome also cleared away a large number of problems which had persisted most of his life. Many of his paranoid characteristics disappeared. He could now recognize that many gestures which he had hitherto considered hostile were, in fact, friendly and complimentary. While not all his obsessional demands were cleared away, he had opened the first large hole in the defensive system. The results were very satisfying and marked the beginning of a successful resolution of a severe obsessional neurosis.

The goals and the treatment plan for the obsessional states can be summarized as follows:

(1) To discover and elucidate the basis for the excessive feelings of insecurity which require absolute guarantees before action is pursued.

(2) To demonstrate by repeated interpretation and encouragement-to-action that such guarantees are not necessary, but that they interfere with living. This requires active assistance in stimulating new adventures for the patient.

(3) To realize that the foregoing is possible only when the patient can acknowledge that anxiety is universal and omnipresent and cannot be permanently eliminated from life. This means abandoning attempts at perfection and superhuman performance and accepting one's humanness with its limitations. It does not mean being mediocre, average, or without ambition. Rather, it allows one to utilize all his assets and potentialities.

Such goals are achieved through the trust and intimacy that grow out of a relationship in which one is sincerely trying to be useful to another human being. However, it also requires skill and intelligence, and the treatment must follow techniques that differ radically from the classical psychoanalytic model. It is important (a) to avoid strengthening the patient's obsessional tendencies, (b) to tailor one's techniques to counter such devices, and (c) to provide a learning experience which may enable hime to alter his defensive patterns. An open, flexible technique with no rigid rules of procedure is demanded—as well as a therapist who is free to experiment and try out modifications in the therapeutic process.

Epilogue

Man lives in a world in which he is only part master. While knowledge and the advances of science have broadened his command over nature, he is still unable to completely control either himself or his environment. He remains dependent on his fellow man and their benevolent concern for his survival, as well as on the impersonal forces of nature that are entirely outside his control. Uncertainties and insecurities pursue his everyday existence, and he has had to settle for some absolutes (such as death) over which he has no influence whatsoever. In more limited ways, he has had to acknowledge his own inability to completely control his own functioning—especially in those areas of physiology and psychology that are outside his awareness.

From the earliest records of human behavior it is evident that much activity has been devoted to attempts to control, influence, and guarantee those forces that are beyond man's

immediate access. The major content of all the primitive re-
ligions was devoted to rituals and devices designed to curry
favor with the gods in order to prevail upon them for some
favorable influence. There were endless ritualistic practices inside and outside of religious systems in which the goal was to
increase man's authority in matters over which he recognized he
had no direct control. These practices were neither subtle nor
devious. They were simple "bargains" in which it was hoped
that fair exchange could be obtained through such performances.
As man's grasp of nature increased and as he developed a growing confidence in his own strength and powers, he developed
more subtle religious practices and more devious devices to
guarantee his living. Monotheism replaced polytheism and man
did not apply for direct aid, but hoped that in his over-all
devoutness and dedication, God would know and minister to
his needs. Later on, he introduced a ministry which interposed
with God for him. He made his religion less a commercial trans-
action and more a moral commitment. Instead of mere exchange
in the form of sacrifices or gifts, he offered a total devotion
in the form of worship. However, when it came to death—
which he could never deny or overcome no matter how powerful or influential he might be—he required a different tactic.
As death could not be overcome, he developed an endless
variety of placating illusions and soporific fantasies of an existence beyond death—even more glorious and fulfilling than the
existence on earth. This folklore served many purposes, but
among them was an evasion of the final acknowledgement of
man's limited meaningfulness in a physical sense and his utter
incapacity to overcome finiteness. It was an evasion of his powerlessness, and Christian eschatology became a social tranquillizer
designed to deal with man's inability to accept the finality of
his biological existence. This type of security operation represented an advance in his intellectual capacities for conceptualization.

When we translate these oversimplified and broad notions
of the role of ritual, religion, and fantasy into the language of

the obsessive-compulsive defense, we can recognize many parallels. The obsessive defenses are attempts to deal with feelings of powerlessness and helplessness in a broad as well as in a limited sense. They represent a private and personal religion in which the ritual attempts to gain a measure of guaranteed living by preventing any possibility of loss of control. As opposed to the ritual designed to influence or control an outer force such as a God, the obsessive ritual is intended to control an inner force which the individual feels he has no capacity to manage. The obsessive device—through its various aspects of procrastination, distraction, indecision, preoccupation with the need to know everything, etc.—is used to establish guarantees and certainties about the future.

The phobia achieves such a result by forbidding any possibility of loss of control in a particular area of living by removing such an area from the individual's existence. It is the ultimate weapon in the struggle to maintain the illusion of control when the fear of loss of control leaves us in danger —either because of what we might do or because of our inability to control what others might do. However, to be effective the phobia must not eliminate too many areas of functioning or it will defeat its purpose and produce a living death (a total isolation from all living).

The attempts at omniscience and omnipotence which are demanded of the obsessional individual frequently lead to grandiose conceptions of himself with consequent expectations of special privilege and exemption from human limitations. This explains much of the behavior of those individuals who are compulsively driven to overeat, or are addicted to drugs or alcohol. The feeling of exemption leads them to deny the inevitable conseuqences of their compulsions. Their expectations of being exempt from the effects of the drug or alcohol or food leads them to believe that they can take them with impunity—or they assume they can control their intake. When trapped in excessive intake, they have grandiose conceptions of their capacity for future control. Thus, addiction results from the magical expectations that also account for these people's inability to profit and learn from their last debauch. Likewise, the psychopath or sociopath—who appears to learn nothing from his previous misadventures and always expects to escape the consequences of his next one—is driven by grandiose conceptions of his invulnerability and exemption from natural laws and cause-and-effect relationships. The grandiosity that accompanies the attempts at obsessional perfection also participates in the delusional processes of the schizophrenic and the paranoid states.

As much of the social and community law that regulates all society requires controls over the participants, the problem of compulsions becomes intimately related to the legal processes as well as to social practices in general. Exemptions, special privileges, and immunity from the laws of man are not available to any person except perhaps the rulers, be they kings or presidents. Consequently, any psychological development that either encourages or sustains a belief in such exemption must inevitably lead the individual into conflict with society in one form or another. In individual terms, it interferes with adequate interpersonal relations and produces gross disturbances in the individual's capacities to sustain fruitful relationships at work, in marriage, in sex, etc. Such difficulties characterize the living of the obsessional. However, in the more extreme situations, when loss of control and grandiose expectations produce antisocial or asocial behavior, the presence of pathologic changes or disease must be taken into account when assessing guilt and punishment. Such interpretations must take into consideration not only psychological or dynamic intrapersonal forces but also the social system itself. Because the obsessional mechanism is triggered not solely by internal forces but is also greatly dependent on the external situation, the political, economic, and social structure of the society must also be taken into account. It is not a question of "who is to blame," but rather an issue of recognizing causes in order to prescribe adequate remedies. In such an instance we see in clear terms the intricate relationship of the internal and external environment in producing neurosis. The cultural nature of neurosis is exemplified in the obsessional neurosis—wherein the individual utilizes his psychological resources to counter insecurities and uncertainties imposed on him by cultural restrictions as well as by his own physiological limitations. Thus the valid administration of justice and the proper use of the legal processes to sanction behavior as well as to eliminate crime and special offenses must incorporate this understanding in all its considerations.

Finally, the full and productive use of man's resources requires that he use the free and fertile skills that he possesses. Freedom has long been recognized as the sod from which the human potentialities can grow fully and mature. While this is widely acknowledged in a political sense, it is only beginning to be understood in a personal and psychological sense. It was not too long ago that the existential and realistic insecurities drove individuals to "escape from freedom" into a false security of obsessional dictates. This is still largely true today. Lack of clarity about the role of compulsions has nurtured the curious but popular notion that creativity or genius springs from neurotic sources and may even be the cause or result of disease. This view is still widely shared by psychologists and writers who draw the inference that since creativity frequently coexists with neurosis, the elements are related in a cause-and-effect manner. However, there are considerable data to suggest that while neurosis and creativity can coexist, the neurotic elements limit and often destroy an individual's creative capacities. In his persistent preoccupation, the obsessive individual often manages great accumulations of knowledge and know-how and can be a first-rate craftsman. However, his rigidity and unwillingness to take intellectual as well as physical risks and his insistence on guaranteed certainties interfere with the novelty and spontaneity so crucial to a truly creative achievement. Compulsions resemble dedication, but they lack the freedom of choice and the spontaneous readiness to change direction which lead to discovery. Creativity is a complex process about which very little is known psychologically. Freud speculated about its relationship to mature sexuality and others have proposed a variety of explanations, including genetic factors. Dedication, hard work, scholarship, and innate talent appear to be critical factors. However, an additional dimension that must obtain once such a combination of elements is present is that of an inner freedom to be open to new experiences without fear or resistance. It is this factor that is lacking in obsessional individuals in spite of their extraordinary capacity for devoted and sustained effort. Their compulsive tendencies limit their openness and curiosity and consequently they are unavailable for new insights and combinations of experience. In a lesser degree we find the precise situation present in all obsessionals whose capacities are seriously limited by their defensive maneuvers. In all such instances, the individual's capacities to produce and to enjoy life's potentialities for joy, discovery, and novelty are restricted.

Treatment, while difficult, is very often successful. It results in a freer, less restricted, and less rigid individual who is no longer tied to "shoulds"—absolute and impossible demands. A capacity to accept the limitations of one's powers and to recognize the impossibility of overcoming certain existential uncertainties, tends to enhance and stimulate activity in the areas of attainable goals. It is not wrong to strive for perfection or to attempt to encompass all that is knowable. It is not arrogant to defy and attempt to overcome the forces of nature both inside and outside the individual. The danger and the disease rest on the *absolute* need to do so—and the inability to compromise once we have discovered that the goal is impossible. The unwillingness to do one's best because it is never perfect (and therefore not good enough) is a disease, while the recognition that one can do only that which one is capable of may stimulate the individual toward heroic efforts to fulfill all his capacities and potentialities. An unwillingness to enter the race because there is no guarantee of winning does not develop a champion but an obsessional neurotic. Only taking the risk of losing permits one to win. Only the readiness for defeat and failure allows an individual to perform in a manner which may ultimately prove successful. This is the difference between functioning at one's best and being *driven* to a kind of "perfection" which makes the individual avoid encounters and contests. Life is a series of risks, uncertainties, and gambles. There are no guarantees and no predictable consequences of our behavior. In the face of a consistency in regard to the universe's major laws, we confront numerous possibilities in regard to its minor principles. To function effectively and productively, we must be satisfied with being able to do the best we can—provided we exert the effort to do just that. The obsessional demand for guarantees does not indicate a higher virtue or a more dedicated conviction; rather it shows an unwillingness to face life with all its possibilities. The existential dilemma which has confused our generation deals precisely with this matter. To be happy, one must risk unhappiness; to live fully, one must risk death and accept its ultimate decision.

INDEX

INDEX

Abraham, Karl, 110, 117, 119
Accuracy, passion for, 35
Acting out in therapy, 241
Adaptation, concept of, 6–7
Addictive states, 162–81, 270–71
  grandiosity in, 165–71
  See also specific addictive states
Aging, aggravation of obsessional
    disorder by, 155–56
Alcoholism, 165–68
  indecisiveness in, 39
Alexander, Franz, 6, 117, 259
Ambivalence, 40–41, 43–49
  depression and, 110
Anorexia nervosa, 175
Anxiety
  in compulsive gambling, 169–70
  definition of, 133–34
  inhibition of sex behavior by, 78
  obsessional defense against, 8–9,
    150
  phobias and, 133, 134–35, 146–47
  provoked by obsessional's work,
    26
  in psychopath, 186, 187
  in therapy, 207, 264
Arrogance, 52
Avoidance reactions, 130–33

Bleuler, Paul Eugen, 43, 151
Bowel training, 12–13, 88
Brain-injured people, rigid behavior
    of, 16
Bruch, Hilde, 175

Children
  adult sexual activities with, 140–41

expression of ambivalent feelings
    by, 45–47
  magical use of language by, 32–33
  obsessive behavior in, 13, 16, 47
  parataxic thinking in, 27
  See also Etiology
Classification of mental disorders,
    3–4, 107–8
Collecting, 93–95
Commitment (involvement), 64–67
Compromise, inability to, 18–19
Confessions
  false, of crimes, 28
  premature, in therapy, 240–41
Control, obsessional's need for
    feeling of, viii–ix, 12, 13, 150
  dependency needs and, 61–62
  in dissipation of anxiety, 8–9
  over emotions, 30–32
  insomnia and, 70
  limitation of commitment and, 65
  need for total control, 16–17, 50
  need to prevent extreme responses,
    49
  sex act and, 78–80, 83
  See also Omniscience
Creativity, 95–97, 272–73
Counter-transference, 209–11, 214
Cultural nature of neurosis, 272
Cultural psychoanalysts, 6–7
Culture in personality development,
    6

Davidson, Henry A., 165 *n*
Death, denial of, 71
Dedication compared with obses-
    sion, ix–x

277